QS-9000 REQUIREMENTS

118 REQUIREMENTS CHECKLIST AND COMPLIANCE GUIDE

Third Edition

Jack Kanholm

AQA Co. ▪ Los Angeles

AQA Co.
155 S. El Molino Av.
Pasadena, CA 91101
Phn: (626) 796 9000
Fax: (626) 796 9070

Printed in the United States of America

To my Father

PREFACE

This book identifies and explains 118 distinct requirements contained in Section I of the QS-9000 standard. The 118 requirements completely translate the whole content of the standard, without leaving anything out. The book interprets the Third Edition (1998) of QS-9000.

The standard is generally vague and nonspecific, and can be difficult to work with directly. This is especially true for the original ISO 9000 text. Some of the 20 sections contain many distinct requirements, often hidden in obscure subsections or phrases, while others contain hardly any. The biggest problem of most QS-9000 implementation projects is that people are not sure, sometimes to the very end, precisely what it is that they have to do to comply. The objective of this book is to take that imprecision and ambiguity out of the standard. This is achieved by reinterpreting the standard with a complete and exhaustive list of precisely stated requirements.

The requirements are phrased in the form of specific actions that need to be taken to ensure compliance. Every requirement is stated in a concise phrase, set in bold type, and followed by an explanation of relevant implementation solutions, content of documentation, requirements for records, and audit practices. Each of these issues is explained under its own heading. Clear organization of the book makes it an ideal reference for planning, documenting, and implementing a QS-9000 quality system, and for preparing a company for the certification audit.

The book is the leading title in the AQA QS-9000 series. The other two books are *QS-9000 Documentation* and *QS-9000 In Our Company* (both written by Jack Kanholm). The role of this book in the series is to introduce the QS-9000 requirements and explain the basic scope of the actions that must be taken to comply. The other books contain more detailed and advanced information on specific topics; namely documentation and training, respectively. The other books of the series are annotated on the last two pages of this book.

The three QS-9000 books are developed from the AQA ISO 9000 series, also authored by Jack Kanholm. The ISO 9000 series consists of four books, three of which have been adapted for the QS-9000 series. The ISO 9000 book that has not been adapted is *ISO 9000 Quality System, Department by Department Implementation for the Certification Audit.* Although it does not include the automotive requirements from QS-9000, it is still an excellent and relevant reference for automotive suppliers. Applicable chapters from *ISO 9000 Quality System* are referenced in this book at the end of every section.

The commercial viability of publishing and distributing this book depends on the copyright protection. Please note that the list of requirements in the first section of the book is also protected. If you need additional copies, please use the order form enclosed at the back of the book, or call the publisher at 626 796 9000.

GOOD LUCK WITH YOUR QS-9000 IMPLEMENTATION PROJECT AND CERTIFICATION OF YOUR QUALITY SYSTEM !

Jack Kanholm

REQUIREMENTS

4.1. MANAGEMENT RESPONSIBILITY

4.1.1 Quality Policy

■ Formulate and document a quality policy, and ensure that the policy is understood and implemented by all personnel at all levels. 14

4.1.2 Organization

■ Define and document the responsibility, authority, and interrelation of key personnel who manage, perform, and verify work affecting quality. 15

■ Appoint an executive manager to be the Management Representative for QS-9000, and define his or her authority. 17

4.1.3 Management Review

■ Conduct scheduled management reviews of the quality system. ... 19

4.1.4 Business Plan

■ Establish and document a business plan. 21

4.1.5 Analysis and Use of Company Level Data

■ Document and analyze trends in quality performance, and compare current quality levels with appropriate benchmarks. 22

4.1.6 Customer Satisfaction

■ Determine customer satisfaction, and compare customer satisfaction levels with appropriate benchmarks. 24

■ Notify certification body or registrar when the customer degrades the status of the site. 25

4.2 QUALITY SYSTEM

4.2.1 General

■ Develop a quality manual documenting the structure, scope, and general policies of the quality system. 28

4.2.2   Quality System Procedures

■ Develop procedures and work instructions explaining how the quality system operates. 30

■ Implement the documented quality system. 31

4.2.3   Quality Planning

■ Use Advanced Product Quality Planning (APQP) methods. 33

■ Organize multi-disciplinary teams for product quality planning. 35

■ Identify special product and process characteristics. 36

■ Mark relevant documents with special characteristics symbols and notations. 38

■ Formally confirm the manufacturing feasibility of proposed products. 38

■ Promote internal awareness of due care and product safety considerations in design and process control policies and practices. 39

■ Develop Process Failure Mode and Effect Analysis (P-FMEAs) for manufacturing processes. 41

■ Use mistake proofing methodologies in planning of processes, facilities, equipment and tooling. 42

■ Establish Control Plans for prototype, pre-launch, and production phases. 43

4.2.4   Product Approval Process

■ Fully comply with all requirements of the Production Part Approval Process (PPAP) manual. 44

■ Utilize a part approval process for subcontractors. 46

4.2.5   Continuous Improvement

■ Improve processes beyond the required capability, with the highest priority on special characteristics. 48

■ Identify opportunities for improvement and implement appropriate improvement projects. 49

■ Develop the knowledge of, and use appropriate measures and techniques for continuous improvement. 51

4.2.6   Facilities and Tooling Management

■ Develop methods for evaluating effectiveness of manufacturing operations. 52

■ Provide adequate technical resources for tool design, fabrication, and inspection; and establish a tooling management system.   53

4.3   CONTRACT REVIEW

4.3.1   General

4.3.2   Review

■ Review contracts and orders to ensure that customer requirements are adequately defined.   55

■ Verify the capability and capacity to meet contract or order requirements.   57

4.3.3   Amendment to Contract

■ Define and document how amendments to contracts are processed and how changes are communicated to functions concerned.   59

4.4   DESIGN CONTROL (only design responsible suppliers)

4.4.1   General

■ Establish a process for selecting and using design information and data from previous design projects.   62

4.4.2   Design and Development Planning

4.4.3   Organizational and Technical interfaces

■ Plan design activities, define organizational and technical interfaces, and assign qualified personnel.   63

■ Demonstrate the skill in, and the use of, appropriate design and engineering techniques.   65

4.4.4   Design Input

■ Identify, document, and review the design input.   66

■ Use computer-aided design and engineering, and ensure interfacing capability with customer computer systems.   67

4.4.5   Design Output

■ Document the design output so that it can be verified against design input requirements, and specify acceptance criteria.   68

■ Review and approve design output documents before release.   69

■ Use appropriate design optimization techniques.   70

4.4.6   Design Review

■ Conduct formal design reviews.   71

4.4.7   Design Verification

4.4.8   Design Validation

■ Verify design at appropriate stages to ensure that the design stage output meets the design stage input requirements. 73

■ Record design validation results, including design failures, and apply corrective and preventive action procedures to address design failures. 74

4.4.9   Design Changes

■ Identify, document, review and approve design changes; and submit changes for customer approval prior to implementation.   75

4.4.10   Customer Prototype Support

■ When required, establish a comprehensive prototype program to validate reliability, durability, life, and other important design characteristics. 77

4.5   DOCUMENT AND DATA CONTROL

4.5.1   General

■ Define the document control system and the types of controlled documents. 80

4.5.2   Document and Data Approval and Issue

■ Review and approve documents prior to issue. 81

■ Identify documents with their revision level, and maintain a master list with current revision status of documents. 82

■ Ensure that current documents are available at all locations where they are needed. 83

■ Remove obsolete documents from points of use and identify retained historical copies of obsolete documents to preclude unintended use. 84

■ Control customer engineering documents and maintain records of their implementation in production. 85

4.5.3   Document and Data Changes

■ Review and approve changes and corrections in documents and reissues of revised documents. 86

■ At distribution, highlight changes in revised documents. 87

4.6 PURCHASING

4.6.1 General

■ When required, use customer-designated subcontractors. 89

■ Ensure that purchased products satisfy safety,
environmental, and other governmental regulations. 90

4.6.2 Evaluation of Subcontractors

■ Evaluate subcontractors, monitor their quality performance,
and maintain records of their quality capabilities and
performance. 91

■ Maintain a list of approved subcontractors. 93

■ Perform subcontractor quality system development with the goal
of subcontractor compliance to QS-9000. 94

■ Require on-time delivery from subcontractors and monitor
their delivery performance. 96

4.6.3 Purchasing Data

■ Precisely and completely describe the ordered products, and
review and approve purchasing documents prior to release. 97

4.6.4 Verification of Purchased Product

■ When appropriate, verify purchased products at subcontractor's premises and afford the same right to your
customers. 98

4.7 CONTROL OF CUSTOMER SUPPLIED PRODUCT

4.7.1 Customer Owned Tooling

■ Establish procedures for verification, storage, and maintenance
of customer-supplied products and customer-owned equipment.   100

4.8 PRODUCT IDENTIFICATION AND TRACEABILITY

■ Identify materials, components, and products during all stages
of production. 102

■ If required, develop procedures for unique identification of
individual products and batches to ensure traceability. 104

4.9 PROCESS CONTROL

■ Plan production activities and processes. 107

■ Ensure that premises are maintained in a state of order, cleanliness and repair. 108

■ Prepare contingency plans to protect supply of product in the event of emergency. 109

■ Develop planned, comprehensive maintenance plan for process equipment and machines. 110

■ Maintain, or have access to, replacement parts for key manufacturing equipment. 112

■ Establish procedures for packaging and preservation of equipment, tooling and gauging. 113

■ Document, evaluate and improve equipment maintenance objectives. 113

4.9.1   Process Monitoring and Operator Instructions

■ Provide process operators with process operating and control instructions. 115

4.9.2   Maintaining Process Control

4.9.3   Modified Process Control Requirements

■ Conduct preliminary process capability studies for all new processes affecting special characteristics. 116

■ Monitor and control processes, especially those affecting special characteristics. 118

4.9.4   Verification of Job Setups

■ Verify job setups, and provide setup personnel with written instructions. 120

4.9.5   Process Changes

4.9.6   Appearance Items

■ Provide qualified equipment and personnel, and maintain masters for processing and verification of Appearance Items. 121

4.10   INSPECTION AND TESTING

4.10.1   General

4.10.2   Receiving Inspection and Testing

■ Inspect or otherwise verify incoming products and prevent them from being used or processed before their conformance is verified. 124

4.10.3   In-process Inspection and Testing

- Carry out in-process inspections to support and validate statistical process control program and other defect prevention measures. 126

4.10.4   Final inspection and Testing

- Inspect finished products to complete the evidence of conformance. 127

- Carry out periodical layout inspections and functional testing. ... 129

- Conduct audits of packaged final product ready for shipment. ... 130

4.10.5   Inspection and Test Records

4.10.6   Supplier Laboratory Requirements

- Establish and document a quality system for in-house laboratories. 132

4.10.7   Accredited Laboratories

4.11   CONTROL OF INSPECTION, MEASURING AND TEST EQUIPMENT

4.11.1   General

4.11.2   Control Procedure

- Calibrate and/or check measuring and test equipment, and maintain calibration records. 136

- Identify, maintain, and safeguard measuring and test equipment. 137

- Reassess validity of previously made measurements when measuring equipment is found to be out of calibration. 138

- Establish and document a quality system for in-house calibration laboratories, and use only accredited commercial calibration facilities. 140

4.11.3   Inspection, Measuring and Test Equipment Records

4.11.4   Measuring System Analysis

- Evaluate all measurement systems referenced in Control Plans. 141

4.12   INSPECTION AND TEST STATUS

4.12.1   Supplemental Verification

- Identify inspection and test status of products, to ensure that only products that have passed required inspections are used or shipped. 143

4.13   CONTROL OF NONCONFORMING PRODUCT

4.13.1   General

■ Identify, segregate, and document nonconforming and
suspect products. 145

4.13.2   Review and Disposition of Nonconforming Product

■ Review nonconforming products and decide whether they should
be accepted, reworked, repaired, regraded, or scrapped. 147

■ Establish and implement a nonconformance reduction plan,
and track progress toward achieving the reduction goals. 149

4.13.3   Control of Reworked Product

■ Provide work instructions for rework operations. 150

4.13.4   Engineering Approved product Authorization

■ Seek customer authorization for shipping product that is
in any way different from currently approved. 151

4.14   CORRECTIVE AND PREVENTIVE ACTION

4.14.1   General

■ Use disciplined problem-solving methods. 154

4.14.2   Corrective Action

■ Establish a system for effective handling of customer
complaints. 155

■ Investigate causes of product, process, and quality system
nonconformances and implement corrective actions. 156

■ Test and analyze nonconforming products returned by
customers. 158

4.14.3   Preventive Action

■ Review process and quality records to identify potential causes
of nonconformances, and implement preventive actions. 159

4.15   HANDLING, STORAGE, PACKAGING, PRESERVATION
AND DELIVERY

4.15.1   General

4.15.2   Handling

■ Use product handling methods and equipment that prevent
damage and deterioration. 162

4.15.3   Storage

■ Provide designated storage areas. 163

■ Control receipt and dispatch of products to and from
storage areas. 164

■ Regularly assess the condition of products in storage. 165

■ Establish and maintain an inventory management system. 165

4.15.4   Packaging

■ Follow customer standards or specify requirements for
packaging and labeling, and control these operations. 166

4.15.5   Preservation

■ Apply appropriate methods of preservation and segregation
of products. 167

4.15.6   Delivery

■ Protect the quality of finished products to include delivery,
when specified in contract. 168

■ Establish a system to ensure consistent on-time delivery
performance. 170

■ Use customer orders, rather than forecasts, in production
scheduling. 171

4.16   CONTROL OF QUALITY RECORDS

■ Index and organize quality records to facilitate their retrieval. ... 173

4.16.1   Record Retention

■ Determine and document retention times for quality records. 175

4.17   INTERNAL QUALITY AUDITS

■ Conduct internal audits using independent and qualified
auditors. 177

■ Implement corrective actions to deal with identified
deficiencies. 179

■ Record and report the results of internal audits. 180

4.17.1   Internal Audit Schedules

■ Plan and schedule internal audits of the quality system. 181

4.18   TRAINING

■ Identify training needs for all personnel. 183

■ Provide for the required training and maintain
training records. 185

4.18.1   Training Effectiveness

■ Periodically evaluate training effectiveness. 186

4.19   SERVICING

■ Apply all requirements of the standard to servicing operations
and activities. 188

4.19.1   Feedback of Information from Service

■ Feedback service concerns to engineering and production. 189

4.20   STATISTICAL TECHNIQUES

4.20.1   Identification of Need

4.20.2   Procedures

4.20.3   Selection of Statistical Tools

4.20.2   Knowledge of Basic Statistical Concepts

■ Identify the need for statistical techniques, establish procedures
for their selection and application, and train personnel in basic
statistical concepts. 191

APPENDIX

■ Checklist of required documents and records. 193

AQA PUBLICATION CATALOG   201

MANAGEMENT RESPONSIBILITY

4.1
Application

Management Responsibility

This section applies to those responsibilities of the executive management that directly affect the quality system and the quality of products and services. Specifically, the management is responsible for defining quality policies and goals, providing suitable organization and adequate resources, and reviewing the adequacy and effectiveness of the quality system.

QS-9000 is a model for a company-wide management system, and as such it must be developed, implemented, and maintained with full consent and support of the executive management. Third-party auditors consider management commitment and involvement to be critical, and will devote considerable time and effort to verify compliance with the requirements and intent of this section.

Documentation

The quality manual should have a section dedicated to management responsibilities. It should contain policies committing management to provide adequate organization and resources necessary to support the quality system, and to periodically review the performance, effectiveness, and continuing suitability of the system. There should also be policies committing management to establish a business plan, analyze trends in quality performance, and determine customer satisfaction levels.

Management responsibilities with regard to quality policy, organization, assignment of responsibilities, and the business plan can be documented completely in the quality manual, without carrying over to operational procedures. The remaining activities — management reviews, analysis of quality performance trends, and determination of customer satisfaction — usually require more detailed instructions, and thus should be further developed in operational procedures.

4.1.1   Quality Policy

Requirement

Formulate and document a quality policy, and ensure that the policy is understood and implemented by all personnel at all levels.

The chairman, president, general manager, or a management committee must formulate a quality policy. It is usually a short statement expressing the general objectives of, and commitment to, the quality system. It can also be a short list of more specific objectives. Companies usually focus their quality policy on commitments to supply defect-free products, to deliver on time, and to continuously improve quality.

Everyone in the company must know what the quality policy is, and be able to explain how he or she contribute to reaching its objectives. It is a good idea to post the policy at conspicuous locations throughout the company so that all employees can familiarize themselves with it. QS-9000 training should also include discussion and explanation of the quality policy.

Procedures

There is no need for operational procedures to satisfy this requirement. The quality policy is usually documented in the quality manual. It is customary to dedicate one of the first pages in the manual for this purpose, and print the policy in bold type in the middle of the page. The policy should be signed by the executive manager who formulated it. The quality manual should also require that all personnel be trained in understanding and implementing the quality policy.

Records

Training records should demonstrate that all personnel were provided with QS-9000 training, including explanation of the quality policy.

Audit

Checking compliance, auditors will verify that the quality policy exists and that it is formally documented. Auditors may ask anyone in the company what the quality policy is and how he or she contributes to attaining its objectives. The policy itself is almost never questioned, unless it is not relevant to quality goals, expectations or needs of customers. For example, auditors could question a policy wherein there is no direct commitment to supply defect-free products, or to continuously improve quality performance.

4.1.2 Organization

4.1.2.1 Responsibility and Authority

Requirement

Define and document the responsibility, authority, and interrelation of key personnel who manage, perform and verify work affecting quality.

A common way to satisfy this requirement is to include in the quality manual the company's organizational charts and specifications of quality-related departmental responsibilities. The charts define organizational units (departments and functions) and their interrelation, while the specifications assign responsibilities and authorities for specific activities.

Although the standard refers only to that part of the organization concerned with quality, it is customary to include organizational charts for the whole company. In larger companies, the general organizational chart can be supplemented by more detailed charts depicting the internal organizations of the QA and/or QC departments.

In addition to the fixed, functional organization there should also be multi-disciplinary teams responsible for quality planning. The quality planning teams are normally defined in those sections of the quality manual and operational procedures dealing with quality planning. However, when the teams are permanent they could be also depicted in the organizational charts.

The requirement for independence (organizational freedom) and authority for quality functions can be interpreted broadly and liberally. Auditors will accept any reasonable organization. In practice, the requirement means that those managing quality should have sufficient authority and should have unhindered and unrestricted access to the executive management.

Third edition of QS-9000 adds to this section a note recommending that "the personnel responsible for quality have the authority to stop production, if necessary to correct quality problems." While this is only a recommendation, auditors will expect that the top manager responsible for quality has such authority. If this is not possible or desirable, someone else independent of production should be formally authorized to make such decision. This authority should be documented.

Procedures

There is no need for a special operational procedure. The general organization is usually defined in organizational charts and specifications of departmental responsibilities, both included in the quality manual. Specific responsibilities for particular activities are documented in the operational procedures that govern those activities. The authority to stop production to correct quality problems can be documented in the quality manual or in the operational procedure dealing with corrective and preventive actions.

Records

No records are required. On the documentation level, the evidence of compliance consists of the organizational charts, and the assignments of responsibilities and authorities in the quality manual and operational procedures. Job descriptions can also be shown to demonstrate that responsibilities and authorities are defined.

Audit

Assessing compliance, auditors will review the quality manual, operational procedures, and job descriptions (if available) to verify that responsibilities and authorities for all functions and activities affecting the quality system are clearly defined. Implementation will be checked by verifying that the designated personnel are indeed involved in decisions, dispositions, and approvals for which they are responsible.

Independence (organizational freedom) of quality functions is almost never questioned. Anyone, including production management and personnel, may share their principal responsibilities with quality functions. Before objecting to any particular organizational structure, auditors must have evidence that there is indeed lack of independence and/or sufficient authority.

Auditors will ask who in the company has the authority to stop production to correct quality problems, and whether this authority is documented somewhere in the system.

4.1.2.2   Resources

There are no unique requirements in this subsection. Training requirements are stated in a more direct and complete manner in Section 4.18, Training. But note, this is the only place in the standard where it is explicitly required that internal auditors must be trained.

4.1.2.3   Management Representative

Requirement

Appoint an executive manager to be the Management Representative for QS-9000, and define his or her authority.

Vice president, director, or manager responsible for quality assurance is a natural choice for the Management Representative. But anyone from management can be appointed, irrespective of his or her other responsibilities. In small companies it is often the president or the managing director. The representative does not necessarily need to have any operational function in the quality system. His or her role is to assume the authority and responsibility for compliance and performance of the system. The minimum requirements for authority and responsibility of the Management Representative are clearly stated in points a) and b), and the NOTE in this Subsection 4.1.2.3 of QS-9000.

Procedures

There is no need for an operational procedure. The appointment of the Management Representative and the authority and responsibilities of this function are usually documented in the quality manual.

Records

Records are not required. The evidence of compliance consists of the documented appointment itself, and of the evidence that the Management Representative is actively exercising his or her authority.

Audit

Assessing compliance, auditors will verify that a Management Representative is appointed, and that he or she is actively involved in implementing and maintaining the quality system.

4.1.2.4   Organizational Interfaces

This subsection is an automotive addition to the original ISO 9000 text. Although deliberately added to the standard, it does not contain any unique requirements.

The system "to ensure management of appropriate activities during concept development, prototype and production" is in fact one of the principal objectives of the QS-9000 quality system, and is thus automatically achieved when the whole system is implemented.

The requirements for "multi-disciplinary approach in decision-making" and "the ability to communicate necessary information and data in the customer prescribed format" are repeated and developed further in other sections of the standard and reference manuals, and will be formulated as specific requirements under appropriate sections.

4.1.2.5   Information to Management

This new section requires that when products or processes become noncompliant, this is promptly reported to the manager responsible for corrective actions. To satisfy this requirement, procedures and/or work instructions dealing with inspections, control of nonconforming product, and process control should instruct inspectors and operators to promptly report any problems to the responsible manager, usually the QA Manager.

4.1.3

Management Review

Requirement

Conduct scheduled management reviews of the quality system.

Management reviews assess the continuing suitability and effectiveness of the quality system in reaching its objectives; i.e., implementation of the company's quality policy and compliance with the QS-9000 standard. The scope of the reviews may comprise such topics as quality objectives, organization, implementation of the system, results of internal audits, effectiveness of corrective and preventive actions, customer complaints, cost of quality, and so forth.

Although not required directly in this Section 4.1.3, the scope of management reviews may be expanded to satisfy many other management-related requirements contained in other sections throughout the standard. For example: review and revision of the business plan, including quality goals and targets (4.1.4); review of company-level quality performance data (4.1.5); review of customer satisfaction data and trends (4.1.6); review of continuous improvement projects (4.2.5); review of corrective and preventive actions (4.14.2); etc.

The reviews must be conducted regularly. Quarterly or half-yearly reviews are recommended for new systems under implementation and maturation. Mature systems can be reviewed on an annual basis. If possible, management reviews should be synchronized with the cycle and timing of internal quality audits.

The most common format for the management reviews is a meeting; but other methods, such as telecommunication conferences, or circulation of reports, memoranda, etc., are also acceptable. The participants should include the top executive management, and managers of such functions as marketing, engineering, production, purchasing, product service and, of course, quality assurance. The third edition If QS-9000 explicitly requires that the Management Review should be conducted with multi-disciplinary approach.

Procedures

A dedicated operational procedure is usually required to set out specific instructions for conducting management reviews. The procedure should define the frequency, participation, and scope for the reviews, and explain how to schedule, conduct, and record the reviews. Smaller companies can try to dispense with the procedure and document everything in the quality manual.

Records

QS-9000 explicitly requires that management reviews be recorded. The nature of the record will depend on the format of the review itself. It can be minutes of a meeting, a memorandum from the executive management, a report with findings and conclusions, etc. The nature of the records and their storage location and retention period should be specified in a procedure. The management review records are the only evidence of compliance. Auditors never have the chance to witness or participate in the reviews. It is, therefore, especially important that the records are properly established and maintained.

Audit

Assessing compliance, auditors will examine the management review records, and will seek to find the evidence that conclusions and recommendations of the reviews are being implemented. It is important that the records clearly document the participation, agenda (scope), and conclusions of the review. Reviewing the participation list, auditors will verify that the reviews are conducted with a multi-disciplinary approach.

4.1.3.1   Management Review - Supplemental

This is a new section in the third edition of the standard. It is a clarification that the Management Review should include all elements of the entire quality system, not only those specifically required in other elements. This is consistent with the purpose of the review, and ISO 9000 has always been interpreted this way.

Although this section does not introduce any new obligations, it reinforces the underlying ISO 9000 requirement that the review be broad and comprehensive. Both the Management Review procedure and Management Review records should support, and demonstrate the implementation of, this principle.

4.1.4   Business Plan

Requirement   *Establish and document a business plan.*

This requirement encourages strategic business planning and development of business goals that drive the continuous improvement process.

The pan should provide short term (1–2 years) and longer term (3 years or more) goals. In addition to the usual market, sales, financial and growth goals, the plan should also include quality-related goals (examples are provided in QS-9000 Section 4.1.4 and QSA Element 4.1-8). The business plan goals should be based on benchmarking developed from analysis of comparable organizations and products inside and outside the automotive industries.

The Third Edition of QS-9000 specifically requires that the business plan must be a controlled document.

Procedures   The standard explicitly requires that the methods to determine current and future customer expectations— and the methods to track, update, revise, and review the plan — must be documented. A dedicated operational procedure is usually required to adequately document these issues. The procedure should name the function, or management team, responsible for establishing the business plan; should explain how benchmarking is used in defining goals; and should instruct how, and how often the plan is tracked, updated, revised, and reviewed. If tracking and revising the business plan is included in the scope of management reviews (refer to the preceding requirement), the procedure dealing with management reviews will also contain some instructions relevant to the business plan. There is also a natural linkage with the continuous improvement system.

Records

The standard does not require that records of business plan reviews be maintained, as it does for management reviews. The business plan itself, with some evidence that the plan is being regularly tracked and updated, will be sufficient to demonstrate compliance. There should also be evidence that appropriate benchmarking is used in defining the goals.

Audit

The standard explicitly states that the content of the business plan is not subject to third-party audit, and that, in some circumstances, cost data may also be withheld from customers. It does not mean that compliance with the business plan requirements will not be audited. Auditors will review the appropriate procedures, will ask to see the cover pages and possibly the list of contents of the plan, and will seek evidence demonstrating that the plan is being tracked, updated, and reviewed. Only the actual data in the business plan are exempted from third-party audit.

4.1.5   Analysis and Use of Company-Level Data

Requirement

Document and analyze trends in quality performance, and compare current quality levels with appropriate benchmarks.

This section requires that quality and operational performance, and other company-level data be systematically collected and analyzed for trends. The elements and features that could be tracked are, for example, scrap and rework levels, process performance, cycle time, cost of non-quality, on-time delivery performance, machine downtime, productivity, and so forth. The requirement to track cost of non-quality is new in the third edition of the standard, and should be implemented when upgrading from second edition. The simplest and most common way to analyze trends is charting data over time and comparing the charts with appropriate benchmarks (development of benchmarks is explicitly required in QS-9000). Management should use the data and trends in decision-making concerning corrective and preventive actions, continuous improvement targets, quality system objectives, and overall business objectives. There is a strong link between this requirement and the requirement for a continuous improvement program (see QS-9000 Section 4.2.5, Continuous Improvement).

Procedures

Although the standard does not explicitly require a procedure for collecting and analyzing company-level data, auditors will expect that at least the scope of data collection and the responsibility for this activity are defined somewhere in the quality system documentation. If a dedicated procedure is not established, the scope and instructions for collecting the data can be included in procedure for continuous improvement or, possibly, corrective and preventive actions. The management responsibility for analyzing and using the data can be included in procedure dealing with the management review.

Detailed instructions will not be expected, unless procedures require use of complex techniques that are not explained elsewhere in the quality system (for example, charting and use of special statistical techniques).

Records

Records and evidence of compliance consist of reports and/or charts documenting trends in company-level quality data, and some form of evidence that management reviews and uses the information (usually provided in the records of management reviews — see Section 4.1.3).

Audit

Verifying compliance, auditors will focus on how the data is collected and processed, and how executive management analyzes and uses the data. Auditors will verify that the data is collected on a regular basis, that it is processed to reveal trends, that it is compared with appropriate benchmarks, and that it is reviewed and used by the management. This element may be audited in conjunction with the preventive action and continuous improvement elements of the quality systems.

4.1.6   Customer Satisfaction

Requirement

Determine customer satisfaction, and compare customer satisfaction levels with appropriate benchmarks.

This automotive requirement calls for a procedure to determine customer satisfaction. The most common way to measure customer satisfaction is conducting customer satisfaction surveys. A satisfaction rating card can be enclosed with each shipped order, or the survey can be conducted periodically. Unsolicited expressions of customer satisfaction or dissatisfaction (complaints) should be considered in determining customer satisfaction level. Results of the surveys should be compared with appropriate benchmarks and be brought to the attention of senior management.

Direct suppliers to Chrysler, Ford and GM receive from their customers periodical performance reports. These reports should be utilized in determining customer satisfaction.

Procedures

The procedure for determining customer satisfaction should define the scope, methodology, and frequency for collecting the relevant data; explain how to analyze the data, compare the satisfaction levels with appropriate benchmarks, and report the results; and assign responsibility for those activities. This procedure can be combined with the procedure for handling and processing customer complaints (QS-9000 Section 4.14).

Detailed instructions will not be expected. However, some companies may find it useful to develop specific instructions explaining how to carry out customer surveys or otherwise collect customer satisfaction data, and how to process and report the data.

Records

The evidence of compliance consists of customer satisfaction surveys, customer performance reports and customer complaints, reports and/or charts documenting trends, comparison benchmarks, and some form of evidence that senior management reviews and uses the information (for example, minutes of management review meetings).

Audit

As was the case with requirements pertaining to the business plan and analysis of company-level data, in this case the audit will also focus on two activities: collection and processing of data, and management review of trends. Auditors will verify that the data is collected in accordance with applicable procedures; that the prescribed frequencies are observed; that the data is properly documented and is compared to appropriate benchmarks; and that senior management reviews and uses the information.

Where customers provide the supplier with periodical performance reports, these reports will be also reviewed by the auditors.

4.1.6.1 Certification Body Notification

Requirement

Notify certification body or registrar when the customer degrades the status of the site.

This requirement pertains only to direct Chrysler, Ford and GM suppliers. It obliges suppliers to notify their certification body or registrar when customer places the site in the status of "Needs Improvement", "Q-1 Revocation" or "Level II Containment", for Chrysler, Ford and GM respectively. The notification must be given in writing and within five business days.

Procedures

There is no need for special operational procedure. It is sufficient for the quality manual to include a statement that the registrar will be notified of any downgrading of the site status by the customer. The manual should also assign the responsibility for issuing such notification (usually the Management Representative).

Records

Records are only relevant when downgrading of status have actually occurred. If so, copy of the notification sent to the registrar will provide the evidence of compliance.

Audit

When auditing direct suppliers to Chrysler, Ford or GM, auditors will always ask what is the current status of the site and whether the status has changed since the last audit. In cases when the status has been downgraded, auditors will ask for a copy of the registrar notification letter.

* * * * *

Further reading

- Standard ISO 9004 Part 1, Sect. 4

- J. Kanholm, *ISO 9000 Quality System*, Chap. 3

- J. Kanholm, *QS-9000 Documentation*: QM Sect. 1 and Operational Procedures AOP-01-01, AOP-01-02, AOP-01-03, MOP-14-02, and QOP-02-07

QUALITY SYSTEM

4.2 **Application**	**Quality System** This section went through significant changes since the initial publication of ISO 9000 in 1987. Initially it contained only references to the overall quality system and its documentation and implementation. In 1994 revision of ISO 9000 a subsection introducing general concepts of quality planning was added. In 1995 QS-9000 further developed the quality planning aspects, completely shifting the focus of this section. And finally, in the third edition of QS-9000, this section is also used to include unrelated requirements that have been previously specified under Section II, Sector-specific Requirements.

QS-9000 only outlines and summarizes the principal quality planning requirements. Detailed requirements and examples of implementation are contained in the "Advanced Product Quality Planning (APQP) and Control Plan" Reference Manual. APQP is frequently referenced in this section of QS-9000 and its use is mandatory. Two other reference manuals that must be used in quality planning are "Potential Failure Mode and Effect Analysis (FMEA)" manual, and "Production Part Approval Process (PPAP)" manual. The APQP manual is a guide for satisfying QS-9000 quality planning requirements. While the use of APQP is mandatory, not all requirements stated in the manual must be implemented. In practice, only those APQP methods that are explicitly named in QS-9000 and in the PPAP manual are mandatory requirements.

Documentation The quality manual should have a dedicated sections for defining the organization and structure of the quality system, for stating general policies and procedures defining the quality planning activities, and for addressing product approval process, continuous improvement, and facilities and tooling management. Although these elements have nothing in common, for historical reasons they happen to be in the same section of QS-9000, and thus should be kept together in the quality manual.

There must be operational procedures providing specific instructions for quality planning, to address multi-disciplinary teams, special product and process characteristics, production trial runs, certification of manufacturing feasibility, establishment of Control Plans, and so forth. QS-9000 and APQP strongly suggest that quality planning activities be divided into a design and prototype phase, pre-launch phase, and production phase. To harmonize with this approach, there should be a separate operational procedure for each phase. Suppliers that are not responsible for design and/or prototype development do not need a procedure for the design and prototype phase.

There must also be operational procedures dealing with product approval process, continuous improvement, and facilities and tooling management.

4.2.1   General

Requirement

Develop a quality manual documenting the structure, scope, and general policies of the quality system.

The quality manual is the top-level document in the four-level structure of the quality system documentation. Its role is to state the general policy of the quality system and the specific policies for each of its elements; to outline the structure of the system; to assign principal responsibilities; and to reference other documents defining the quality system, especially the operational procedures.

Much of the information contained in the quality manual will be repeated and further developed in the operational procedures. For this reason, some companies do not see any added value in having the manual as a separate document, and either combine it with operational procedures or reduce its contents to meaningless paraphrasing of QS-9000 requirements. But even though the manual may look just like a summary of the operational procedures, it has an important independent role. It states the principal policies and presents the outline of the quality system for the benefit of those in the company who will further develop and document the system, and those from outside the company who may require general information about the company's quality system — customers, for example.

A well-written and presented quality manual is a powerful marketing tool. It can be enclosed with offers and be otherwise distributed for promoting the company. To serve this purpose well, the manual should be brief but at the same time sufficiently developed to vividly present the quality system. It should also project the quality culture and image of the company.

The quality manual is usually divided into the same 20 sections as the QS-9000 standard Section I. Requirements of Section II, Customer-specific Requirements, can be either incorporated under appropriate elements of Section I, or be addressed in separate sections added to the manual. Such organization ensures that all requirements will be addressed systematically without missing anything. Even when a section or a requirement is not applicable, it should still be included with a heading and an explanation why it does not apply.

Subsectional headings are also important. Headings from the standard should be used in organizing the manual whenever practical and possible. This approach ensures that the documentation is "audit friendly," i.e., can be quickly correlated with the QS-9000 standard for assessing compliance. The QSA (Quality System Assessment) Document Review section contains a list of quality system elements that auditors should be able to identify in the quality manual. The list is a mixture of sectional and subsectional headings of QS-9000.

Procedures As the quality manual is the top-level document, there is usually no procedure explaining how to write it.

Records

The only relevant records are authorized approval signatures in the manual and a distribution record (actually required in Section 4.5 rather than this section). The evidence of compliance is the quality manual itself.

Audit

Compliance audit is carried out in two phases. First, the manual is submitted to the registrar (or other auditing authority) for a desk study where it is examined to verify that it satisfactorily addresses all QS-9000, PPAP, and other relevant requirements of the the automotive reference manuals. Then, the manual is assessed again for adequacy during the audit, i.e., when it can be judged in the context of the environment in which it is used.

4.2.2   Quality System Procedures

Requirement

Develop procedures and work instructions explaining how the quality system operates.

Operational procedures constitute the second level of the quality system documentation. Procedures define the systems (what and when), designate the responsible personnel (who), and provide system-level instructions (how). The distinction between operational (or system) procedures and work instructions is that procedures explain activities, while work instructions provide specific steps for accomplishing a task. For example, an operational procedure for calibration will explain who is responsible for managing the calibration activities, how measuring and testing equipment is inventoried and how its calibration status is tracked, what are the rules for recall of defective equipment, and so forth. A calibration work instruction will explain how to calibrate a specific type of measuring instrument. Work instructions are often called procedures — for example, welding procedure, painting procedure, or calibration procedure. It can be confusing, but there is no reason to abandon the traditional nomenclature as long it is clear which kind of procedures are second-level documents and which belong in the third level. Work instructions will be discussed in Sections 4.5 and 4.9.

A typical operational procedure should include a distribution list, an explanation of its purpose, a definition of its application, specific rules and instructions for carrying out the activity that is the subject of the procedure, and a clear assignment of authorities and responsibilities pertaining to the activity. Procedures also must be uniquely identified by a title (and/or code number) and revision level, and must be formally released by an authorized function, usually on management level.

Procedures

Some, especially larger, companies have a procedure explaining how to write procedures. Although not required, it can be a useful tool to ensure that procedures follow a certain standard and contain all of the relevant and required information. If such procedure was established, it would be included under Section 4.5, Document and Data Control.

Records

The only relevant records are authorized approval signatures on procedures and a distribution record (actually required in Section 4.5 rather than this section).

Audit

As a general rule, registrars require that operational procedures be submitted for a desk study together with the quality manual. They are assessed in the same manner as the manual. The procedures are first examined for compliance with QS-9000 and the automotive reference manuals and then, during the audit, they are assessed again for adequacy in the context of the environment in which they are used.

Requirement

Implement the documented quality system.

This otherwise obvious requirement expresses an important principle: Compliance with QS-9000 can only be achieved when all documented procedures are implemented, including those that may exceed the requirements of the standard. Implementation is audited against the quality system documentation rather than the standard itself. Auditors look back into the standard only when a QS-9000 requirement is not fully addressed in the procedures.

Irrespective of third-party and customer audits, companies operating QS-9000 quality systems are obliged to verify internally that their system is implemented and that it is effective. The main elements of this verification are internal quality audits and management reviews, including evaluation of trends in quality performance and customer satisfaction data. As a rule, third-party auditors will not certify a quality system without the evidence that at least the first internal auditing cycle is completed, and that the executive management has reviewed the system.

Procedures

There is no need for an operational procedure. It is sufficient that the quality manual states the commitment to implement the quality system.

Records

While the principal records of implementation are internal audit reports and records of management reviews, all records created by the quality system provide the evidence of its implementation.

Audit

The whole scope of third-party or customer audit aims to determine whether the quality system is implemented. This is the purpose of the audit. However, even though it is the job of auditors to assess compliance, they will require that, prior to their audit, the company have audited itself and determined that the quality system is implemented.

4.2.3   Quality Planning

The original ISO 9000 standard makes a general reference to quality planning and quality plans, but the requirements are not very specific. In the ISO 9000 text of this section the list a) through h) does not contain any unique requirements that are not restated in other sections of the standard. The list is included to highlight the types of activities that should be considered when designing the quality system. In QS-9000 the quality planning aspects have been developed much further to become one of the most important elements of the standard. The following five requirements are all automotive additions to the original ISO 9000 text.

4.2.3.1

Advanced Product Quality Planning

Requirement

Use Advanced Product Quality Planning methods.

Advanced Product Quality Planning process and methods are described in the APQP Reference Manual. QS-9000 explicitly requires that the manual be used. However, not every APQP requirement must be implemented. The mandatory requirements are those that are also stated in either the QS-9000 standard itself or in the PPAP manual. Everything else can be considered as a guide.

The APQP manual suggests that quality planning be divided into the following five phases: preliminary product and process planning, product design verification, process design verification, product and process validation, and production feedback assessment. An alternative approach is to divide the process into three phases corresponding to the three types of Control Plans — prototype, pre-launch, and production — that are explicitly required in QS-9000. The advantage of the three-phase approach is that it focuses on the Control Plans as the output of the quality planning process in each phase.

The APQP manual discusses over 40 activities associated with quality planning. Not all of those activities are relevant in all cases, and their importance will also vary depending on the nature of particular products, processes, and other circumstances. The most important, mandatory activities that must be carried out at appropriate phases of the quality planning process are those activities that are explicitly required in the QS-9000 standard (not limited to Section 4.2) and are required for the Production Part Approval Process (PPAP). For example: Special Product Characteristics, Design FMEAs, Prototype Control Plan, Special Process Characteristics, Process Flowchart, Process FMEAs, Process Operator Instructions, Measurement System Analysis, Pre-launch Control Plan, Production Trial Run, Process Capability Study, Production Control Plan, Team Feasibility Commitment, and Quality Planning Sign-Off.

The list is not exhaustive. Looking at APQP as a process for preparing the PPAP submission is probably the most efficient way to comply with the quality planning requirements.

Procedures

Several procedures are usually required to document the quality planning process. One procedure should explain how the overall process operates, i.e.: what are the quality planning phases; how are the multi-disciplinary quality planning teams organized and what are their responsibilities; what are the core inputs and outputs of the process; how are the automotive reference manuals used; how is the output of the process documented and communicated; etc. This general procedure should be supplemented by more specific procedures explaining the quality planning activities in each phase. The use of specific quality planning tools and techniques, such as FMEA or Control Plan Methodology, can be explained in work instructions, or by reference to appropriate sections in the automotive reference manuals.

Records

Product quality planning will typically result in hundreds (if not thousands) of pages of studies, reports, plans, and communication documents. All of them will evidence compliance, but the most essential are the Control Plans. Other key documents to show auditors are lists of special characteristics; FMEA studies; feasibility commitment; process capability studies; measurement systems evaluation reports; quality planning sign-off; and other such documents, reports, and records evidencing that all activities comprising the quality planning process are being carried out.

Audit

The audit will concentrate on documentation and record review, as it is not likely that auditors will have the opportunity to witness prototype testing, or process qualification activities (although this may happen). It is therefore important that the relevant documentation is well-organized and easily retrievable. It helps when documents and records are identified by the same names as used in QS-9000 and APQP, so that there is a direct correlation between the requirements and the documents demonstrating their implementation. Auditors will verify that the program and documentation are sufficient in scope (as per APQP manual and internal procedures), and will note whether documents are properly reviewed and approved.

Requirement

Organize multi-disciplinary teams for advanced product quality planning.

Advanced product quality planning and/or review of the resulting studies and Control Plans must be carried out by a multi-disciplinary team (often referred to as the APQP team). The team should include representatives from quality assurance, engineering, production, servicing, purchasing, sales, and other relevant functions as appropriate. Customers and major subcontractors should also be included when appropriate. The team can be either permanent or it can be organized for individual projects. The functions represented on the team should have defined roles and responsibilities. In some cases, the customer may help with establishing the APQP team.

Key responsibilities of the APQP team are selection of special characteristics, development of FMEAs and establishment of actions to reduce failure risks for modes with high risk priority numbers, and development or review of Control Plans. In addition, the team can be responsible for feasibility reviews, design reviews, management reviews, and other activities requiring cross-functional or multi-disciplinary approach.

The APQP reference manual contains detailed guidelines pertaining to multi-disciplinary teams and their responsibilities. While the principle of multi-disciplinary approach must be implemented, the specific system presented in the APQP manual may be modified to suit particular organizations.

Procedures

An appropriate operational procedure should explain how the multi-disciplinary quality planning team is organized, which functions are represented, how the team operates, and what are its main responsibilities. If the team is permanent, the procedure can directly name its members. Otherwise, when the team is assembled for specific projects and/or is different in each phase, the procedure should explain the policy for selecting team members and assign the responsibility for organizing the teams.

Records

The record evidencing compliance consists of memoranda, procedures, minutes of meetings, and other such documents that define the composition of the team and identify its leader, and provide the evidence that the team is actively operating.

Audit

Verifying compliance, auditors will review documents and records pertaining to the organization of the team and its work, and will interview members of the team. If an important function is excluded from the team — a major subcontractor, for example — auditors will want to know whether this was an omission or a deliberate decision. (Subcontractors do not have to be included, but there should be a rational explanation why a major subcontractor is not represented.)

4.2.3.2   Special Characteristics

Requirement

Identify special product and process characteristics.

Special product characteristics are usually identified in the product design stage as those characteristics that are important for product safety, compliance with government regulations, fit and function, and appearance. Special process characteristics are those process input variables that affect variation in special product characteristics.

The concept of special characteristics is central to QS-9000. The standard calls for early identification of special characteristics and prescribes specific systems and techniques for controlling them. Special product characteristics, and sometimes also process characteristics, are identified by customers in drawings and specifications. In addition to the customer-defined characteristics, suppliers are expected to analyze products and processes to further identify additional special characteristics. Customers use unique symbols and notations to identify special characteristics. They are explained in QS-9000 Section II, Customer-specific Requirements; and in APQP Reference Manual Appendix C — Special Characteristics Symbols.

The APQP multi-disciplinary team is responsible for developing or finalizing special product and process characteristics. The selected characteristics must be formally documented and approved.

Procedures   Appropriate operational procedure for quality planning should explain how special characteristics are identified (customer requirements and in-house input), and who is responsible for identifying, documenting, and approving the characteristics (APQP team and customers). Methods for changing and updating the selection of special characteristics should also be defined in the procedure.

Records   The evidence of compliance consists of lists, forms, or other types of documents specifying the selected special product and process characteristics. A form for documenting special characteristics is provided in the APQP Reference Manual, Supplement K.

Audit   Verifying compliance, auditors will examine documents defining special product and process characteristics, noting whether the selection has been formally reviewed and approved. Auditors will also review supporting documents and interview appropriate personnel to understand how special characteristics, especially process characteristics, are selected. They will ask for process flow charts, process FMEAs, timing charts, process capability studies, and so forth. The attention is likely to focus on special process characteristics because these are normally selected by the supplier.

Requirement

Mark relevant documents with special characteristics symbols and notations.

This automotive requirement calls for special marking of those procedures and instructions pertaining to processes and inspections that affect special characteristics. The documents are to be marked with the customer's special characteristics symbols. The symbols are explained in QS-9000 Section II, Customer-specific Requirements, and in Appendix C.

The types of documents that are likely to fall into this category are FMEAs, Control Plans, process operator instructions, setup instructions, SPC instructions, and inspection procedures.

Procedures

There is no need for special operational procedure. It is sufficient that the quality manual contains a general commitment to implement this requirement.

Records

The evidence of compliance is the actual marking of relevant documents with the special characteristics symbols.

Audit

While reviewing documents, auditors will note whether procedures and instructions affecting special characteristics are appropriately marked.

4.2.3.3   Feasibility Review

Requirement

Formally confirm the manufacturing feasibility of proposed products.

Although inserted in this Section 4.2.3, Quality Planning, this requirement really pertains to Section 4.3, Contract Review. The requirement calls for a formal review and analysis of the capability to meet contract requirements. The APQP team, or other multi-disciplinary team, is asked to certify that the specification can be met, that the required tolerances are attainable, that the manufacturing processes are stable and capable, that statistical process control methods are used to monitor process performance, that products can be manufactured without incurring unusual costs for capital equipment and tooling, and so forth. Confirmation of the manufacturing feasibility must be documented using the Team Feasibility Commitment form provided in Appendix L of the APQP reference manual. All members of the APQP team — or at least those representing engineering, production, and quality assurance functions — must sign the commitment. The feasibility commitment should be signed off before contracting to manufacture the products.

Procedures

An appropriate operational procedure should explain when, how, and who should perform the manufacturing feasibility evaluation, and how the conclusion is to be documented. The procedure must either define the scope of the evaluation and provide a sign-off form, or it can simply refer to the Team Feasibility Commitment form included in the APQP manual.

Records

The record and evidence of compliance consist of the properly filled out and signed off Team Feasibility Commitment form.

Audit

Assessing compliance, auditors will verify that manufacturing feasibility evaluations are carried out for every proposed contract, and that the conclusions are properly documented and signed off. Members of the APQP team may be interviewed and asked about the specific methods and data used in the evaluation. Auditors will also note the date when the feasibility commitments are signed off, to verify that this is done prior to the acceptance of corresponding contracts.

4.2.3.4   Product Safety

Requirement

Promote internal awareness of due care and product safety consideration in design and process control policies and practices.

This new automotive requirement (QS-9000 Third Edition) obliges suppliers to develop and implement policies promoting the awareness and consideration of the safety aspects of their products. This specifically applies to activities related to product design and production process control.

In design, due care and safety considerations should be reflected in design input specifications, in design reviews, and in design verification and validation. Engineering personnel should be aware of the safety consequences of failure or malfunctioning of the product.

In production, personnel should know which special product and process characteristics have been so designated because of safety considerations. Process operators should be also aware of the consequences of product failure, especially those failure modes that could be caused by defective materials or inappropriate processing.

Although this is not explicitly required, companies designing and/or manufacturing products that are directly related to vehicle safety would be advised to provide product safety awareness training to all personnel, regardless of their function. This kind of training is widely implemented in such industries as medical device manufacturing.

Procedures

There is no need for a dedicated operational procedure to satisfy this requirement. To comply, the quality manual should include policies committing the company to consider, and promote the awareness of safety aspects of the product. The policy to consider safety could be included in sections dealing with quality planning, design, and process control; and the policy to promote awareness could be included in sections dealing with training. Procedures corresponding to these sections of the manual should further reinforce and support the policies.

Records

Records and evidence of compliance consist of design input specifications, design review records, design verification and validation reports, process operator instructions, notes on drawings and other technical documentation, and training records.

Audit

Assessing compliance, auditors will review relevant policies stated in the quality manual and procedures, and will ask how, specifically, product safety is considered in product design and manufacture. To verify awareness, auditors will review training programs and records, and will interview personnel about their knowledge of the safety aspects of the products and the consequences of product failure.

4.2.3.5   Process FMEAs

Requirement

Develop Process Failure Mode and Effect Analysis (P-FMEAs) for manufacturing processes.

Process FMEAs are normally developed in the pre-launch phase of the quality planning process. The analysis must consider all process characteristics and process input variables that affect special product characteristics. The FMEA methodology is explained in the Potential Failure Mode and Effect Analysis (FMEA) reference manual. Unless there are any reasons to do otherwise, the whole FMEA manual can be adopted into the quality system documentation as a work instruction explaining how to prepare and use FMEAs.

Procedures

The operational procedure dealing with development and use of Process FMEAs should assign the responsibility for establishment and review of the FMEAs (the APQP team), and explain how improvement actions are developed and implemented to achieve lower risk priority levels. The procedure should emphasize defect prevention over defect detection. For detailed technical instructions on how to carry out and document the analysis, the procedure can refer to the FMEA manual.

Records

Record and evidence of compliance consist of completed FMEA reports. The FMEA manual provides special forms for development of FMEAs. Additional evidence of compliance are reports demonstrating that appropriate process improvement actions are being implemented when the FMEAs turn out high risk priority numbers.

Audit

Assessing compliance, auditors will verify that FMEAs are prepared for every new production and when there are substantial changes in the production environment and/or setup. Auditors will also review the FMEAs to verify that appropriate actions are being developed and implemented in a timely manner when the risk priority numbers are high.

4.2.3.6   Mistake Proofing

Requirement

Use mistake proofing methodologies in planning of processes, facilities, equipment and tooling.

Mistake proofing is designing or setting up equipment or processes in such a way that making a mistake becomes impossible. It can be a mechanical feature, such as guides, keys, gates, etc. that force operators to carry out the process in only one, predetermined way. It can be software that stops or locks an operation when it is done incorrectly or when operational parameters are outside of specification. It can be arrangement of processing, transfer, feeding or other equipment in a way to force material flow in a predetermined way. Any process or design feature that eliminates the possibility of manufacturing a nonconforming product is mistake proofing.

This requirement emphasizes mistake proofing as the preferred and, when applicable, required method for reducing risks of product nonconformances. It is again mentioned in Section 4.2.5.3, Techniques for Continuous Improvement.

Procedures

There is no need for a special procedure. Operational procedures dealing with quality planning, corrective and preventive actions, and continuous improvement should name mistake proofing as the preferred method for dealing with potential sources of nonconformances.

Records

Relevant records are documents related to quality planning (especially FMEAs) and reports of preventive and corrective actions, that demonstrate the use of mistake proofing methods to deal with potential sources of nonconformances.

Audit

Auditors will review FMEAs, process capability studies, and corrective action reports, and will verify that, when appropriate, mistake proofing methods were used to prevent and resolve problems.

Auditors may ask outright to be shown specific examples of the application of mistake proofing methods. Therefore, companies preparing for the audit are advised to identify mistake proofing features in their equipment and processes, and make sure that relevant personnel are aware of what mistake proofing is and where it has been applied.

4.2.3.7   The Control Plan

Requirement

> *Establish Control Plans for prototype, pre-launch, and production phases.*

QS-9000 explicitly requires documented Control Plans for prototype, pre-launch, and production phases. The Control Plans are developed on the basis of the output from quality planning activities. The plans identify special product and process characteristic, and specify the process control, inspection, and testing measures that will be employed in each phase to control variation of these characteristics and to detect nonconformances. Control plans must be approved by the customer, unless this requirements is waived (see PPAP manual).

The methodology for establishing Control Plans is described in detail in the APQP reference manual. Unless there are any reasons to the contrary, the entire APQP Section 6.0, Control Plan Methodology, can be adopted as instruction for establishing the Control Plans.

Procedures

Appropriate operational procedure should explain when establishment of new or revised Control Plans is required;

who is responsible for establishing the Control Plans for each phase (must be a multi-disciplinary team, usually the APQP team); how the plans are established (methodology); how they are documented, approved, and issued; and how the plans are distributed and used (they are usually included in process operator instructions, see Section 4.9.1). The procedure should also explain how the Control Plans are revised and amended in response to changes in product design, process performance, quality performance history, etc.

Records

The record and evidence of compliance are the Control Plans themselves. Additional evidence is provided by all backup documentation developed in the course of the quality planning process, for example, FMEAs, process capability and performance reports, measurement system evaluation reports, inspection procedures, and so forth.

Audit

Auditors will verify that Control Plans are established for all three phases (prototype, pre-launch, and production) for new products, and that the plans are reviewed and updated in connection with product and/or process changes, and when processes become unstable or non-capable. Auditors will also note whether the plans have been developed by a multi-disciplinary team, and have been approved (including customer approval when required) and released prior to commencement of mass production. Members of the team may be interviewed and asked about the methodology used for developing the Control Plans.

4.2.4   Product Approval Process

4.2.4.1   General

Requirement

Fully comply with all requirements of the Production Part Approval Process (PPAP) manual.

The PPAP manual requires that a complete submission of part approval must include the following 14 items: 1) warrant; 2) appearance approval report; 3) two sample parts; 4) engineering design documentation and records; 5) engineering change documents; 6) complete layout inspection report; 7) special inspection and testing aids; 8) material, performance and durability test reports; 9) process flow charts; 10) design and process FMEAs; 11) control plans; 12) process performance evaluation reports; 13) measurement system evaluation reports; and 14) design engineering approval. Some items do not apply in certain cases. For example, items 4, 5, 14, and design FMEAs do not apply when suppliers are not design responsible.

Depending on the submission level assigned by the customer, some of the 14 items must be submitted directly to the customer for review and approval. The remaining items are retained at the manufacturing location and must be made available to the customer and QS-9000 auditors upon request. One of the objectives of a QS-9000 audit is to verify that the items retained at the manufacturing location have indeed been completed and are established in accordance with the requirements of the PPAP manual and other reference manuals.

Procedures   While a procedure for preparing and submitting the PPAP package is generally expected, such procedure would convey very little new information. The 14 PPAP submission items are established in the course of various activities regulated by the quality system, especially product quality planning, and are already documented in other procedures. The actual PPAP process and its requirements are documented in great detail in the PPAP manual. The only issues that need to be documented is a policy committing the company to comply with the PPAP requirements, and assignment of responsibilities for coordinating the submission package. This could be done in the quality manual alone.

However, whether it makes sense or not, an operational procedure for PPAP is expected by auditors and customers, and thus should be established. The procedure would assign the responsibilities for coordinating the submission and interfacing with the customer in related matters; reiterate the main requirements for the original submission and subsequent revisions to address product or process changes; and describe how, and to what extent, PPAP submission is required of subcontractors, and how it will be evaluated, verified and approved (refer to the next requirement).

Records

Records and evidence of compliance are the required submission items. These can be in the form of reports, declarations, samples, engineering documents, etc., as appropriate. All items must be reviewed, approved, and issued as controlled documents.

Audit

Auditors will verify that all required items have been established, whether or not they had to be actually submitted for direct customer approval. Reviewing the documents, auditors will check that the information is complete and has been established in compliance with requirements of the PPAP and other reference manuals. Auditors will also verify that all documents have been internally reviewed and approved by authorized functions.

4.2.4.2   Subcontractor Requirements

Requirement

Utilize a part approval process for subcontractors.

This is a new requirement introduced in the third edition of QS-9000. It obliges suppliers to establish a formal part approval process for their subcontractors. In general, the part approval process for subcontractors does not need to be the same as required in the PPAP (Production Part Approval Process) manual. Suppliers can establish their own part approval process as long as it is generally compatible with PPAP and is appropriate to the nature and criticallity of the subcontracted product. However, some customers may require PPAP to be passed down directly, as does General Motors in QS-9000 Section II, Customer-specific Requirements.

The part approval process for subcontractors must be formally documented. This documentation should contain requirements and instructions for the subcontractors, and an operational procedure explaining how to process and approve subcontractor submissions.

Subcontractor instructions may be in a form of a manual, specification, procedure, or be included directly in the contract. If the PPAP process is passed dow unchanged, or with minor modifications, the PPAP manual itself can be referenced in the contract.

Procedures

The operational procedure should explain how the subcontractor part approval submission is handled and processed internally. It should define which elements of the submission must be reviewed and approved prior to first production shipment; who is authorized to approve the submission; how is the authorization granted, and how and when it can be withdrawn; how to process requests for exemptions and who has the authority to make these decisions; and so forth. The procedure should also instruct how to establish and maintain pertinent review and approval records.

Records

Records and evidence of compliance consist of the actual part approval applications submitted by subcontractors and records of their processing, review and approval.

Audit

Assessing compliance, auditors will first verify that there are documented requirements and a process for subcontractor part approval, and that they satisfy customer-specific requirements, if any, and/or are appropriate to the nature and criticallity of the subcontracted product. Then, auditors will review a sample of contracts to verify that part approval requirements are formally stated, or are referenced in contracts. Finally, auditors will review a sample of the actual submissions, verifying that they are complete; that they have been processed and approved in accordance with applicable procedures; and that they are updated as required, especially in conjunction with subcontractor production process changes and customer engineering changes (refer to Section 4.2.4.3).

4.2.4.3   Engineering Change Validation

This is a new section introduced in the third edition of the standard. It reinforces the general requirement that engineering changes must be validated using relevant elements of the PPAP process, or in conjunction with a wider customer validation program (e.g. new model introduction). There are no new obligations in this section. These requirements are clearly stated in the mandatory PPAP manual; or would be included in the contract.

The NOTE in this section reminds that the requirement to validate engineering changes must be passed down to subcontractors, and thus be included in their part approval requirements (refer to the preceding section).

4.2.5   Continuous Improvement

Requirements of this section apply to all activities that bear on product quality and productivity. For example: improvement of processes, reduction of nonconformances, improvement of resource allocation, improvement of on-time delivery, reduction of machine downtime, reduction of labor and material waste, and so forth.

4.2.5.1   General

Requirement

Improve processes beyond the required capability, with the highest priority on special characteristics.

The third edition of the standard has substantially reworded and somewhat redefined the general approach to continuous improvement. It emphasizes that improvement of processes to attain required capability or performance cannot be credited toward continuous improvement because it is, per definition, a corrective action. Following this logic, the standard now explicitly requires that "the supplier shall develop a prioritized action plan for continuous improvement in processes that have demonstrated stability, acceptable capability and performance." The priority must be set on processes responsible for special characteristics.

This new approach and the direct "shall" statements remove any doubt whether improvement of processes beyond the specified capability is required or not. It is, albite not for all processes simultaneously. The prioritization should focus on processes responsible for special characteristics.

Procedures

The quality manual section dealing with continuous improvement and appropriate operational procedure should require that processes be continuously improved beyond the minimum specified process capability. The procedure should provide guidelines for selecting processes for further improvement and assign the responsibility and authority for this decision. The actual process improvement and process performance monitoring activities are usually explained in other procedures, such as those for studying process capability or statistical process control. The improvement projects can be initiated and implemented, and their effectiveness verified, using a system similar to the corrective and preventive action system.

Records

The record and evidence of compliance are specific action plans to improve process capability, and evidence that processes performance is continuously improving over time.

Audit

Auditors will review process control charts and note whether process performance is generally improving over time. Auditors will also ask directly to be shown specific action plans to improve particular processes, and will verify that the planned actions are implemented, maintained and monitored.

4.2.5.2   Quality and Productivity Improvements

Requirement

Identify opportunities for improvement and implement appropriate improvement projects.

This section contains a list of 16 examples of quality and productivity improvement projects that could be considered for the continuous improvement program. The list is only indicative. Companies can select projects appropriate to their needs and resources, except for two kinds of projects that must be operated permanently by all suppliers: improvement of process capability and reduction of product nonconformances (both are identified as mandatory in other sections of the standard).

The system for identifying improvement opportunities should be integrated with such activities as management reviews, development of the business plan, analysis of customer satisfaction, review of company-level data, process performance monitoring, corrective and preventive actions, and internal auditing. In the framework of management reviews, the executive management can be made responsible for selecting and initiating improvement projects (see Procedure AOP-01-03 and QOP-02-07 in the *QS-9000 Documentation* software).

Procedures

Procedure dealing with continuous improvement should explain how improvement opportunities are identified and improvement projects are implemented. One practical way is to list all those activities that provide quality and productivity performance data and to assign the responsibility for periodical review of the data to identify opportunities for improvement. The procedure should also provide a system for tracking results of improvement projects.

Records

The evidence of compliance are memoranda, minutes of meetings, reports, etc., that identify opportunities for improvement. There should also be improvement project files demonstrating that projects are being implemented, and records showing that they are effective.

Audit

Auditors will ask about specific improvement projects and review records of their implementation and effectiveness. They will also glance through the company-level quality performance data to verify that improvement opportunities are being identified where appropriate. The continuous improvement element will usually be assessed at the very end of the audit, when auditors themselves have identified the weak areas. Knowing how the quality system performs, they will be in a position to judge whether the system for identifying improvement opportunities works effectively.

4.2.5.3

Techniques for Continuous Improvement

Requirement

Develop the knowledge of, and use appropriate measures and techniques for continuous improvement.

This section contains a list of 9 continuous improvement measures, methodologies, and techniques that suppliers should be familiar with and use as appropriate for investigating improvement opportunities and implementing improvement projects. Even though some of the listed techniques may not be relevant and are not used, suppliers should demonstrate the knowledge of all 9 techniques, without exception. The concern is that when a technique is not known it will never be used, whether it could be relevant or not. In practice, to satisfy this requirement, there must be at least one person in the organization that is familiar with a technique. Preparing for the audit, companies should compile a list of personnel that can demonstrate that knowledge.

Procedures

The continuous improvement procedure should list all 9 techniques and oblige the quality manager, or someone else, to maintain a list of personnel knowledgeable in the techniques.

Records

Records are not explicitly required, although education and training records would be helpful to demonstrate the knowledge of the listed techniques.

Audit

Auditors will select a sample of the continuous improvement techniques from the list and ask for evidence or demonstration that the company is knowledgeable in the techniques. If there are no relevant training or educational records, auditors will want to interview those that have the knowledge. They will ask how the knowledge was acquired, and how it is applied in specific improvement projects. Auditors may also ask a couple of questions about a technique to verify the knowledge of the interviewed person.

4.2.6   Facilities and Tooling Management

4.2.6.1   Facilities, Equipment, and Process Planning Effectiveness

Requirement

Develop methods for evaluating effectiveness of manufacturing operations.

The effectiveness of manufacturing operations, as specified in this section, should be evaluated with respect to material flow and handling, operator and line balance, automation, value-added labor content, inventory levels, and human factors. Other aspects may be added as appropriate. For every aspect listed above suppliers must develop methods for evaluating effectiveness. Most of these aspects have already been addressed in other elements of the quality system; for example, quality planning. The production trial run and the quality planning sign-off are excellent platforms for carrying out the operational effectiveness studies and for multi-disciplinary certification that the effectiveness is satisfactory. For those aspects that are not studied during the production trial run, additional effectiveness studies should be conducted (for example: inventory levels, or line balance).

Procedures

A dedicated procedure for planning and measuring the effectiveness of production operations may not be necessary. Production planning issues and verification of efficiency may have been already addressed in procedures dealing with quality planning, process control, and continuous improvement. The quality manual can document the relevant policies and refer to those activities and operational procedures that apply. A special procedure can be justified when there are efficiency studies in the program that are not already documented in other procedures.

Records

Records and evidence of compliance are flowcharts, memoranda, minutes of meetings, reports, etc., demonstrating that production operations are planned, and that their effectiveness is evaluated.

Audit

Assessing compliance, auditors will review plant layouts, process flowcharts, material flowcharts, and other such documents that may be presented as evidence of production planning. Auditors may also ask specifically how operator and line balance was evaluated, for example. Suppliers should be ready to answer such specific questions for each aspect of operational efficiency that is named in this section.

4.2.6.2   Tooling Management

Requirement

Provide adequate technical resources for tool design, fabrication, and inspection; and establish a tooling management system.

The system for ensuring compliance with this requirement will depend on how much tool design and fabrication is involved, how extensively tooling is used, and how complex is the tooling.

The first part of the requirement, calling for appropriate technical resources, is rather vague and is not readily auditable. To demonstrate compliance, it is sufficient to use qualified tool designers and machinists, adequate fabrication equipment, and to verify tools before they are used in production. Drawings used in tool fabrication must be controlled to the same requirements as are applied to product drawings and specifications.

The second part of the requirement may be much harder to comply with. It calls for a documented tool management system, including maintenance, repair, recovery, storage, setup, and tool change program. Some of the elements are already required in other sections of QS-9000. For example, tool setup and change interval instructions are required in Section 4.9, Process Control. The standard does not specify any particular requirements or criteria for the tooling management system.

Procedures

A dedicated operational procedure should outline tool design, fabrication, and verification requirements; and/or instruct how tooling subcontractors should be qualified and controlled. The procedure should also provide a tool management system, to be used in tool maintenance, repair, storage, and recovery. Tool setup and tool change programs are usually documented in procedures and work instructions pertaining to process control.

Records

Records and evidence of compliance are tool drawings, maintenance logs, tool and tool setup verification reports, tool inventories, and so forth.

Audit

Auditors will verify that tools are designed and fabricated by qualified personnel and in a controlled environment. They will focus on tool testing and other verification activities, and on measures to prevent tools that are not fully verified from being used in production. Auditors will also review the tool management system, focusing on such aspects as tool inventory system, tool status identification, protection of tools in storage, and identification of customer owned tools (must be permanently marked). Tool setup instructions and verification, and tool change programs are usually audited in connection with other process control elements.

* * * * *

Further reading

- Standard ISO 9004 Part 1, Sect. 5
- J. Kanholm, *ISO 9000 Quality System*, Chap. 2
- J. Kanholm, *QS-9000 Documentation*, QM Sect. 2, and Operational Procedures QOP-02-01, QOP-02-02, QOP-02-03, QOP-02-04, QOP-02-05, QOP-02-06, QOP-02-07, and OOP-02-08

CONTRACT REVIEW

4.3   **Contract Review**

Application

Requirements of this section apply to contracts and purchase orders received from customers.

Documentation

The quality manual should have a section dedicated to contract review. It should contain policies committing the company to verify that customer requirements are adequately defined, and that the company has the capability and capacity to meet these requirements. The manual should also contain a short outline procedure explaining how the policies are implemented, and reference the operational procedures that apply.

There must also be at least one operational procedure explaining how contracts and purchase orders are reviewed. Companies that sell standard catalog products and custom products would probably want to have a different procedure for each.

4.3.1   **General**

4.3.2   **Review**

Requirement

Review contracts and orders to ensure that customer requirements are adequately defined.

The review system addressing this requirement will vary significantly depending on the nature of the product, type of contract and the manner in which it is received, and the relationship between the supplier and the customer.

The simplest contract is an order for a catalog product stocked by the supplier (or a partial shipment of custom products that have been already approved by the customer). In this case, the review will consist of verifying that the ordered items are precisely identified and there can be no doubt what the customer wants. At the other extreme, the contract may be for design and delivery of a complex custom product, such as an entire system of a vehicle. In the case of such custom products, the contract review will be naturally integrated with the whole process of contract negotiations, involving site visits, meetings with the customer, conceptual technical proposals, and a program of drawings and parts approval. In cases where design is involved, many of the contract review activities will overlap with design input verification activities required in Section 4.4.4. Some aspects of product quality planning and PPAP submission activities can be credited to contract review.

In the special case of verbal orders, the orders should be confirmed. The customer can either be given a written confirmation, or the order can be verbally repeated back to verify that the customer's requirements have been well understood.

Procedures

The operational procedure dealing with contract review for standard products, or established custom products, can be fairly specific. It would instruct on how to receive and route orders; appoint personnel responsible for conducting order review; determine the scope of the review; define what will constitute the review record; and instruct how the order requirements are to be communicated to other concerned functions.

The contract review procedure for custom products is usually more general. Because the scope of the orders and the way in which they are received may vary considerably, the objective of the procedure will be assigning responsibilities and providing a general system, rather than detailed instructions.

Records

Records are discussed in the last subsection.

Audit

Assessing compliance, auditors will review a sample of orders to verify that they were reviewed prior to acceptance. They will also inspect PPAP submission records and records of returned products and customer complaints, noting whether there are cases of wrong part being submitted or shipped, caused by inadequate understanding of customer requirements.

Requirement

Verify the capability to meet contract or order requirements.

Assessment of the capability to meet customer requirements should verify, as appropriate, that the specification can be met, that the required tolerances are attainable, that the manufacturing processes are stable and capable, that statistical process control methods can be used to monitor process performance, that products can be manufactured without incurring unusual costs for capital equipment and tooling, and so forth. Availability of materials, and equipment and manpower capacity, should also be verified. Other aspects that may require capability verification are special packaging and delivery requirements, special quality requirements (appearance items, for example), environmental and safety requirements, and so forth.

The scope of the verification can vary considerably. In the simplest case of standard catalog products sold from stock, the verification can be limited to checking if the ordered products are available for shipping. At the other extreme, when complex custom products are involved, the verification of the capacity to meet requirements often becomes a project in itself, involving cross-functional input, subcontractors, and customers.

A similar requirement for verification of capability to supply ordered products has already been stated in Section 4.2.3.3 of QS-9000, wherein the supplier is required to formally review and certify manufacturing feasibility. Although the requirement in Section 4.2.3.3 pertains to product quality planning, the resulting Team Feasibility Commitment also fully satisfies this requirement for capability and capacity verification in contract review. The Team Feasibility Commitment can thus simultaneously satisfy both the quality planning and contract review requirements.

Procedures

The operational procedure dealing with contract review for standard catalog products, or for shipment of established, previously accepted custom products, should instruct what specific steps must be taken to verify that the ordered products are in stock, or can be manufactured before the requested delivery dates. The procedure should also designate the function(s) responsible for conducting the verification, and instruct how to establish the verification record.

In the case of custom products, the procedure could be more general. Custom orders can vary considerably from one order to another, and a detailed and rigid system may not be appropriate. The procedure should aim at establishing a general system for communicating data and information between the sales department and other concerned departments (production control, engineering, etc.), rather than prescribing specific order processing steps.

When manufacturing feasibility reviews are conducted and are concluded with Team Feasibility Commitment (required in QS-9000 Section 4.2.3.3), the procedure should refer to and recognize these activities as an integral part of the contract review process.

Records

Records are discussed in the last subsection.

Audit

Assessing compliance, auditors will review a sample of orders and/or contracts to verify that they were reviewed prior to acceptance. Auditors will note whether there is a history of unusual difficulties with meeting specifications or process capability requirements and, if so, they will investigate further to find out why these problems were not anticipated and whether this indicates inadequate verification of the manufacturing capability at contract review.

4.3.3 — Amendment to a Contract

Requirement

Define and document how amendments to contracts are processed and how changes are communicated to functions concerned.

The system for processing change orders usually parallels that for accepting new orders. Change orders are matched with the initial orders, and are reviewed for adequacy and completeness of stated requirements, and for the capacity to meet the changed or additional requirements.

The major difference between the processing of initial orders and that of change orders is in communicating the changes to the functions concerned. While initial orders are usually fed into the system at one end and are then sequentially processed by various departments, change orders may need to be communicated simultaneously to many departments. To accommodate changes, it may be necessary to intercept the processing of the initial order in design, production control, production, and/or shipping; withdraw from these locations any documents superseded by the changes; and replace them with revised documents.

Procedures

The operational procedure governing the review and processing of change orders should address the issues highlighted in the preceding two paragraphs. It should instruct how to receive and route change orders; designate personnel responsible for their review; instruct in the scope of the review; define what will constitute the record of the review; and instruct on how change order requirements are communicated to other concerned functions.

Records

Records are discussed in the last subsection.

Audit

Assessing compliance, auditors will review a sample of change orders and the evidence of associated communication with the customer and within the company. The audit will verify that change orders are being reviewed; that they are formally accepted and authorized before implementation; and that all concerned functions are promptly informed about the changes.

4.3.4   Records

Throughout this book, records are discussed directly in connection with every requirement. However, in this case the standard contains a subsection specifically dedicated to records, thereby forcing the change of this organization. The only other place where this happens is Section 4.10. The existence of a subsection dedicated to records has no special significance. It does not mean that records are not required, or are not as important, in other elements of the quality system. It only means that not much thought has been given to the organization of the original ISO 9000 standard. Subsectional divisions are often quite arbitrary throughout the whole standard.

The simplest way to establish a contract review record is to initial and/or stamp REVIEWED or ACCEPTED directly on the customer's order. When the review is more complex and involves different departments, a feasibility commitment can be circulated for sign-offs, or the conclusion of the review can be recorded in a memorandum or minutes of a meeting. In fact, any form of record is acceptable as long as it provides the evidence that an order or a contract has been reviewed.

When manufacturing feasibility reviews are conducted and are concluded with a Team Feasibility Commitment (required in QS-9000 Section 4.2.3.3), the feasibility commitment certification can be used directly as a record of contract review. A sample of the Team Feasibility Commitment form is included in APQP reference manual Appendix L.

* * * * *

Further reading

- J. Kanholm, *ISO 9000 Quality System*, Chap. 4
- J. Kanholm, *QS-9000 Documentation*, QM Sect. 3, and Operational Procedures MOP-03-01 and MOP-03-02

DESIGN CONTROL

4.4   Design Control

4.4.1   General

Application

This section applies only to design responsible suppliers. The design control requirements apply to design and development of the final products purchased by, or intended for sale to, customers. General research and development activities that are not intended to directly support the design of a specific product can be excluded from the system.

The distinction between research and development and design activities can be often blurred. To determine if a given activity must comply with the requirements of this section, the following question should be asked: Is the development/research activity intended to support the design of a specific product, or is it a search for new ideas and solutions that, if successful, may be used in future designs? The requirements of this section are only mandatory in the first case.

Documentation

The quality manual should have a section dedicated to design control. It should contain policies committing the company to plan and organize design activities, identify and document design input, conduct design reviews, control design output, and verify the design. The manual should also contain a short outline procedure explaining how the policies are implemented, and reference the operational procedures that apply.

On the procedure level, there must be at least one operational procedure explaining the design control system. In companies that have different types of design projects (for example, improvements of existing products and development of entirely new products), each type is usually covered by a separate procedure. Additional, project-specific procedures may also be needed for special design projects, especially large projects with participation of many external consultants, or projects that are otherwise unusual for the company.

4.4.1.1   Use of Design Data

Requirement

Establish a process for selecting and using design information and data from previous design projects.

This is a new requirement introduced in the third edition of the standard. It obliges suppliers to establish a formal system for selecting, approving and using information and data from previous design projects of a similar nature. In practice, engineers always use archived design files when developing a new design project, and there is nothing new in that. However, the use of such information by the design team is usually informal. The intent of this requirement is to formalize this activity.

Procedures

The wording "The supplier shall have a process to . . ." strongly implies that there must be a procedure regulating the research, selection, review, approval and use of information and data from previous projects. Such procedure should assign a specific responsibility for researching and selecting relevant information and data, and require that the information be reviewed and formally approved before release to the design team. Such review would check that the data was previously verified and validated, that the historical design was performing satisfactorily, and that the information is indeed relevant to the current design project. In principle, the information and data from previous projects should be researched, reviewed and controlled in the same way as the design input (refer to Section 4.4.4). This procedure could be included as a section in the general Design Control procedure.

Records

The record and evidence of conformance consists of reports, memos, minutes of meetings, cover letters, etc., identifying the information and data from previous projects that are relevant to the new design, and authorizing specific historical documents to be used for this purpose.

Audit

Assessing compliance, auditors will review the applicable procedure, and verify that the use of information and data from previous design projects is adequately controlled. Walking through the engineering department, auditors will look out for historical drawings and project books that are apparently being used in the current design, and will investigate whether these materials have been formally reviewed and are authorized for use.

4.4.2   Design and Development Planning

Requirement

Plan design activities, define organizational and technical interfaces, and assign qualified personnel.

To satisfy this requirement, every design and development project should be divided into individual design activities grouped into design phases; the activities and phases should be scheduled out; qualified personnel should be assigned to each activity; and the technical interfacing (communication of information and data) between various internal and external design groups should be formally coordinated. Design activities should also include design reviews, verifications, and validations.

For a simple routine design project, all these requirements can be addressed using a one-page design project plan. The plan should list all design activities (including reviews, verifications, and validations) and for each activity should identify the assigned personnel or team, relevant design input references, the required output, and the start and completion dates. Such a design project plan not only satisfies the requirement for design project planning, but also addresses requirements pertaining to design input and output, and design verification. Example of such design project plan is provided in the *QS-9000 Documentation* software.

For large and complex design projects, a more sophisticated project management system will be expected. It should include such elements as critical path scheduling, project organization charts, transmittal letters and acknowledgments, logs tracking transmittal and receipt of documents and information, schedules for release of drawings and specifications, procedures for progress and design review meetings, and so forth.

Procedures

For simple and routine design projects, the operational procedure dealing with design planning can be quite specific. It can instruct how to develop a design project plan, and assign the responsibility for establishing and tracking the plan.

When projects are more complex and their scope and nature can vary considerably, the procedure should be more flexible. Instead of providing detailed instructions, it should outline the general system for managing design projects, and require that more detailed, project-specific procedures be established for individual projects.

For large projects with participation of many external consultants, several procedures may be required to establish a comprehensive system for design project management. The elements that need to be considered are planning, scheduling, communication of information and data, and assignment and coordination of design activities.

Records

Records and evidence of compliance are provided by the documents established in the course of planning and scheduling design projects.

Audit

Checking compliance, auditors will review a number of design project books and/or files to verify that all documents required by procedures are being established. They will also verify that project schedules, activity plans, assignment of personnel, and definition of technical interfaces are all documented for each design project. Auditors may also ask for evidence that the assigned personnel are qualified (see next requirement).

QS-9000 REQUIREMENTS 65

4.4.2.1   Required Skills

Requirement

Demonstrate skills in, and use of, appropriate design and engineering techniques.

This section lists about a dozen design and engineering techniques, and requires that design activities be qualified in those techniques when appropriate. Definitions of the acronyms and short explanation of the techniques can be found in the APQP reference manual, Appendix B. While the standard does not emphasize any one of the listed techniques, the FMEAs and, to a lesser degree QFD and DOE, are also mentioned in many other sections of QS-9000 and the automotive reference manuals.

Procedures

The design procedure should mention all relevant design and engineering techniques; point out the reference manuals, books, and other sources where information about the application of the techniques can be found; and encourage the use of these techniques in the design process. In larger organizations, or in conjunction with complex design projects, it may be appropriate to provide engineers with formal training. In any event, the supplier must be able to demonstrate that design engineers are knowledgeable in the use of the techniques.

Records

The record and evidence of compliance consist of diploma, certificates, training records, or other form of evidence that design engineers are qualified in the use of appropriate design and engineering techniques. Self-study certification could be sufficient. Training programs and records are further discussed in Section 4.18.

Audit

Verifying compliance, auditors will review the list of design techniques used by the supplier, will examine records demonstrating qualifications of design engineers, and will review design files to verify that appropriate design techniques are indeed used in actual design projects. Auditors may also want to interview engineers to verify their knowledge of relevant techniques.

4.4.3 **Organizational and Technical Interfaces**

Requirements of this section are discussed under preceding Section 4.4.2, Design and Development Planning.

4.4.4 **Design Input**

Requirement

Identify, document, and review the design input.

Design input requirements are the expected features and characteristics of the product being designed. It can be its weight, size, appearance, performance, resistance to environmental conditions, serviceability, energy consumption, emission or noise level, and so forth. Cost is also an important characteristic.

Design input is defined by a customer. The customer can be internal or external. An internal customer is usually the marketing or business development department that, based on market research, specifies new product briefs, which are then used as design input. An external customer is either the end user, another company, or another division.

QS-9000 requires that the design input be formally documented (even when the customer is internal) and be reviewed by the designers for adequacy and completeness. Any ambiguous or conflicting requirements should be resolved before the design input requirements are used in developing the design. Changes or amendments to the design input should be likewise reviewed and approved.

This requirement for documenting and reviewing design input parallels the requirement for contract review (see Section 4.3.2). In fact, design input is often defined in the technical sections of a contract and thus, its preliminary review is usually carried out within the scope of contract review.

Procedures

Operational procedure governing the control of design input should define how the design input is documented; who approves it; what constitutes the record of approval; how to distinguish an approved document from a preliminary document; how the design input is communicated to the design team; and how changes in the design input are documented, approved, and communicated.

Records

Records and evidence of compliance are provided by documents defining the design input for current and completed projects.

Audit

Checking compliance, auditors will review a number of design project books and/or files to verify that design input documents are being established and approved in accordance with procedures. They will also assess the manner of transmitting the design input requirements to individual design teams. Handling of design input changes will be also investigated.

4.4.4.1   Design Input - Supplemental

Requirement

Use computer-aided design and engineering, and ensure interfacing capability with customer computer systems.

This automotive requirement obliges suppliers to use computer-aided design and engineering systems, so-called CAD and CAE. Supplier's systems must be compatible with those used by the customer, to allow for two-way interface and data transfer. In some cases customers may provide preliminary drawings and design input data on a computer disk or via on-line connection. This requirement for using CAD/CAE systems may be waived by the customer.

Procedures

There is no need for an operational procedure — it is sufficient to state in the quality manual a general commitment to use CAD/CAE systems in design.

Records

The only relevant record is the evidence that the CAD/CAE system is compatible and capable of interfacing with the customer system. This could be a letter from the customer, or a demonstration that disks provided by the customer can be used in the system.

Audit

Verifying compliance, auditors will visit the CAD/CAE computer stations, and may ask for a demonstration that the system is capable of interfacing with the customer system. While in those areas, auditors may also verify compliance with other requirements pertaining to computers; for example, validation and approval of computer software, and document control system for computer files.

4.4.5   Design Output

The original ISO 9000 part of this subsection contains a list of three requirements. Tow of them, however, namely points a) and c), will not be further discussed in this book as separate requirements. Regarding point a), auditors normally do not engage in the actual verification that the design output meets the design input requirements, but instead rely on design verification records (see Section 4.4.7). Regarding point c), the requirement to identify Special Characteristics is stated more directly and forcefully elsewhere in the standard and the APQP manual. In any event, Special Characteristics are usually identified by customers.

Point b), regarding acceptance criteria, is discussed in the following requirement.

Requirement

Document the design output so that it can be verified against design input requirements, and specify acceptance criteria.

Design output is usually documented in drawings, specifications, bills of materials, parts lists, instructions, procedures, and so forth. Almost all companies today, especially those implementing QS-9000, document their design output, and thus automatically satisfy the first part of this requirement.

The requirement for verifyibility and acceptance criteria is only new and unique in the ISO 9000 part of the standard. In QS-9000 it has been earlier expressed in much more specific terms in Section 4.2.3, Quality Planning. Both the FMEAs and the Control Plans must contain or reference acceptance criteria. Compliance with the quality planning requirements automatically ensures that this requirement pertaining to design output is also satisfied.

Procedures

The procedure dealing with design control should contain a section dedicated to design output. The procedure should require that the design output be fully documented and, although not explicitly required in QS-9000, that the scope of the design output documentation should be planned in advance. With regard to the acceptance criteria, the procedure may refer to FMEAs and Control Plans.

Records

The design output documents themselves, together with FMEAs, Control Plans, and associated inspection and testing procedures, provide the evidence of compliance.

Audit

Checking compliance, auditors will ask how acceptance criteria are defined and/or referenced (or will read about it in a procedure), and will review a sample of relevant documents to verify implementation. Auditors will pay special attention to those acceptance criteria that are expressed in terms of samples and workmanship standards. The samples must be reviewed, approved, and otherwise controlled like all other design output documents.

Requirement

Review and approve design output documents before release.

Review of design output documents should not be confused with design verification. The kind of review required in this section is often called engineering inspection. The purpose of the review is to check and coordinate drawings, specifications and other design output documents to ensure that they are complete and correct. But this is not verification of the design itself — a faulty design can still be well documented. The review and approval of design output documents should be evidenced by a signature of an authorized function, and the approved documents should be controlled in accordance with QS-9000 Section 4.5, Document and Data Control.

Procedures

The quality manual should state the policy that all design output documents are reviewed and approved before release, and an appropriate operational procedure should explain in detail how this policy is implemented. The procedure should define who is responsible for reviewing the documents and who has the authority to approve them; provide guidelines regarding the scope of the review; instruct how to establish the review records (sign-off on documents, in a log, etc.); and explain how to distinguish approved documents from preliminary and other documents that are not approved for use in production.

Records

Records and evidence of compliance are provided by the review and approval sign-offs in the design output documents or in logs, etc.

Audit

Assessing compliance, auditors will look for approval signatures on design output documents. In fact, auditors always check for authorizing signatures whenever they see a drawing, specification, or other engineering document. It is a reflex.

4.4.5.1   Design Output - Supplemental

Requirement

Use appropriate design optimization techniques.

This section lists five categories of engineering techniques to be used for optimizing the design. While it expresses an important requirement that the design process should include efforts to optimize, simplify, innovate, and reduce waste by using modern design and engineering techniques, the requirement is not readily auditable by a third-party assessment. It is difficult to prove that there has been no effort made to simplify the design, for example.

The word *shall* in the first sentence of this paragraph indicates that all five categories of the listed engineering techniques must be implemented in every design project. While it is unlikely that auditors will expect a formal report for each type of study and analysis named in the list, suppliers should be prepared to demonstrate that indeed each one was employed in design. Design FMEAs are always mandatory as they are also required for the PPAP submission.

Procedures

At a minimum, the operational procedure dealing with design control should instruct which engineering optimization techniques must be used in the design process. All relevant techniques mentioned in QS-9000 should be listed. In addition, the procedure could assign specific functions for carrying out the studies, and define reporting requirements.

Records

The record and evidence of compliance consist of reports with results of the optimization analysis and studies. In cases when formal studies are not carried out, but the optimization techniques are used in discussions (during a design review meeting, for example), the evidence may consist of minutes of meetings or memoranda mentioning that such discussions have taken place.

Audit

Reviewing project files, auditors will ask for the evidence that all relevant optimization techniques listed in QS-9000 Section 4.4.5 have been employed in the design process. It is unlikely that auditors will expect a formal report for each type of study. Except for FMEAs, there are no specific format or reporting requirements for the studies. However, to be convincing, there should always be something in writing (see paragraph above).

4.4.6　　Design Review

Requirement

Conduct formal design reviews.

The purpose of design reviews is to assess and verify the evolving design at appropriate stages. Design reviews should not be confused with design project coordination and management activities, although both can be conducted at the same meeting. Design reviews should consider adequacy of the design input; reliability goals; production and inspection feasibility; design verification and

72 QS-9000 REQUIREMENTS

validation; and so forth. The reviews should also evaluate efforts to optimize, simplify, and innovate, and assess the results of Design FMEAs, QFD, DFM/DFA, DOE, and other such studies. Another important function of design reviews is tracking of design verification progress (see reference to DVP&R in the APQP manual).

Design reviews must be planned in advance and be included in the design project schedules. The meetings are conducted by the design team, but must also include representatives from other concerned functions. The team conducting design reviews is often the same as the team responsible for quality planning (APQP Team). In fact, quality planning and design reviews are often conducted at the same meetings.

QS-9000 does not explicitly state how many, or at which design stages, design reviews must be conducted. The generally accepted interpretation is that even a smallest design project should have at least two design reviews: one following the planning and design input review stage, and the other in conjunction with the final approval of the design. Larger projects would typically have a regularly scheduled design review meeting — for example, weekly or monthly — depending on the nature and pace of the project.

Procedures

The operational procedure regulating design reviews should define who is responsible for scheduling design reviews; determine who will participate in the reviews; provide guidelines for establishing the agenda for the reviews; and instruct how the design review records should be established.

Records

Establishment and maintenance of design review records are explicitly required in the standard. Minutes of design review meetings or reports with their conclusions are the most popular formats. Records should state who participated in the review, what aspects of the design were reviewed, and what are the conclusions and recommendations of the review.

Audit

Assessing compliance, auditors will examine the design review records pertaining to a sample of current and completed design projects. Auditors may also follow up on some specific conclusions and recommendations to check if they were implemented.

4.4.7   Design Verification

4.4.8   Design Validation

Requirement

Verify design at appropriate stages to ensure that the design stage output meets the design stage input requirements.

Design verification requirements parallel those for product verification. Just as product should be inspected when passing from one production stage to another, so should the design. A design stage output is used as design input in the next design stage. The standard requires that the output be verified before it is used and/or released.

Design verification must go beyond an engineering inspection, i.e., coordination and checking of drawings and specifications to detect errors and omissions. Design verification concerns the adequacy of the design itself.

When design reviews are conducted at appropriate stages of design, this requirement for design verification is basically satisfied. Design reviews are a form of design verification. In addition to design reviews, the standard suggests four other ways to verify a design stage output: alternative calculations, comparison with a similar proven design, tests and demonstrations, and review of design stage documents.

Procedures

A relevant operational procedure should explain how design verification is planned and how the plan is documented; what verification methods will be employed; and how the verified design stage documents are approved for use and/or release. If design review is the most frequently used design verification method, the procedure can be combined with the one governing design reviews. But it is always good to have a *Design Verification* heading in the procedure to quickly establish that the requirement is addressed.

Records

Design verification must be recorded. This is explicitly required in the standard. The record should identify the person or team that carried out the verification and should specify what verification methods were employed. The verified design stage documents should be also authorized for use and/or release.

Audit

Assessing compliance, auditors will review a sample of design project files, noting whether feasibility studies, preliminary drawings, calculations, and other design stage documents have been verified and approved. They will also check that engineers and other design personnel use approved design stage input documents in their current work.

4.4.8.1   Design Validation - Supplemental

Two independent requirements are raised in this new subsection added in the third edition of the standard. One concerns synchronization of design validation activities with customer's wider system validation or other prototype programs, and other concerns documentation of design failures and application of corrective and preventive actions to address these failures.

From the point of view of a quality system, the first requirement is not really relevant, or even auditable, as synchronization of design validation activities with customer's prototype programs is really a contractual matter. However, to cover this point, the quality manual should include a statement expressing a general intent to cooperate with the customer in timing the design validation program.

Requirement

Record design validation results, including design failures, and apply corrective and preventive action procedures to address design failures.

The requirement to record design validation results is obvious and is already expressed in ISO 9000. The true intent of this new section is to ensure that the entire history of design failures and changes to address these failures are documented.

A somewhat curious part of this requirement is the obligation to apply corrective and preventive action procedures to address design failures identified at the stage of design validation, i.e., before the design is approved and released for production. The standard is clear in its intent to require that actions to correct design failures must be formally planned and documented, but application of the general corrective and preventive action procedure for this purpose is not customary. For many companies it will make more sense to develop an independent engineering procedure for analyzing and correcting design failures.

Procedures

To comply with these requirements, the Design Control procedure should clearly instruct that all design validation results, including design failures, must be documented. This procedure should also define a system for correcting design failures, or refer to the general Corrective and Preventive Action procedure.

Records

Records and evidence of compliance consists of reports, memos, and other documents established in the course of validating the design and correcting design failures. The record should include the entire history of design failures and actions to address these failures.

Audit

Assessing compliance, auditors will review the procedure for addressing and correcting design failures, and will specifically ask for records demonstrating implementation of this procedure.

4.4.9   Design Changes

4.4.9.1   Design Changes - Supplemental

Requirement

Identify, document, review, and approve design changes; and submit all changes for customer approval prior to implementation.

Identification of required or desired design changes may come from many different sources inside and outside the company. The system for processing and implementing design changes should provide internal departments, customers, and users with channels designated for requesting changes. The system should also define the process of evaluating the requests and deciding if they should be implemented. Once a request for change is accepted, the remaining activities — implementation of the change and verification of the changed design — should basically follow the same procedures that apply to original designs.

With regard to automotive application, QS-9000 explicitly requires that design changes must be approved in writing by customers before their implementation in production. Further specific requirements with regard to implementation of design changes are included in the PPAP reference manual.

Procedures

The operational procedure dealing with design changes should provide forms, or prescribe other means, for identifying and documenting design changes; provide guidelines for evaluating change requests; and explain how design changes are implemented and verified.

Records

Records and evidence of compliance consist of all documents established in the course of initiating and implementing design changes. Forms used for initiating and documenting design changes are often referred to ECRs or ECNs.

Audit

Assessing compliance, auditors will review change order files and engineering change requests (ECRs), noting whether they are all established and processed in compliance with procedures. Auditors will compare approval and implementation dates to verify that changes are not implemented prior to formal customer, or other authorized, approval.

4.4.9.2   Design Change Impact

This new section added in the third edition of QS-9000 requires that the supplier should consider the impact of design changes on the system in which the product is used. Specific methods and procedures to implement this requirement will depend on the nature of the product, the supplier's knowledge of the larger system, and the contractual relationship. To cover this point, the quality manual and/or appropriate operational procedure should include a statement expressing intent to evaluate the impact of design changes on the wider system. Where appropriate, the Engineering Change Notice (or Request) form could also have a check-box to indicate whether this evaluation is relevant and was carried out.

4.4.10   Customer Prototype Support

Requirement

When required, establish a comprehensive prototype program to validate reliability, durability, life, and other important design characteristics.

Validation of design is usually performed on a prototype of a product, by testing it under real or simulated operating conditions. The validation is performed to confirm that the design satisfies the expected user needs and/or requirements with regard to performance, safety, durability, reliability, life, serviceability, and other such characteristics.

When required, the supplier must have a comprehensive prototype program. Prototype testing should be planned and documented in prototype Control Plans, per requirements of QS-9000 Section 4.2.3 and the APQP Reference Manual. The plan should prescribe specific testing procedures for each anticipated mode of use and the tested characteristic. The results of prototype testing must be recorded. Additional specific requirements with regard to design validation and prototype testing are also included in the PPAP reference manual.

Procedures

The operational procedure dealing with design control should have a section dedicated to design validation and/or prototype testing. The procedure should assign the responsibility for coordinating validation activities, require establishment of detailed testing instructions, and define who and how should evaluate test results.

In addition to the operational procedure there may be a need for specific testing instructions for each anticipated mode of use and tested characteristic. The instructions should explain the setup, testing parameters, data collection and analysis, and reporting. For relatively simple tests the Control Plans may be sufficient to provide such instructions.

Records

Results and conclusions of design validation testing must be recorded. The format and content of prototype testing reports should be defined in specific testing procedures (instructions).

Audit

Assessing compliance, auditors will review the design validation and prototype testing procedures and reports. They will also want to visit the testing areas (make sure that only calibrated measuring equipment is used there).

4.4.11   Confidentiality

This new section added in the third edition of QS-9000 requires that the supplier shall ensure confidentiality of customer-contracted products under development. Normally, to cover this point, it is sufficient to include in the quality manual and/or appropriate operational procedure a statement that confidentiality of customer-contracted products under development will be ensured. Where required in contract or otherwise applicable, more specific measures, such as stamping documents CONFIDENTIAL, restricting access to documents and development areas, etc., may need to be implemented.

* * * * *

Further reading

- Standard ISO 9004 Part 1, Sect. 7 and Sect. 8
- J. Kanholm, *ISO 9000 Quality System*, Chap. 5
- J. Kanholm, *QS-9000 Documentation*, QM Sect. 4, and Operational Procedure EOP-04-01

DOCUMENT AND DATA CONTROL

4.5.
Application

Document and Data Control

This section applies to documents, not records. To clarify any possible confusion, a document is a policy, procedure, instruction, plan, drawing, specification, etc., containing instructional information and data on how the quality management system functions, how activities and tasks are to be carried out, and how to build products and provide services. A record, by contrast, is a written statement of facts pertaining to a specific event, person, process, product, and so forth. Control of records is addressed in Section 4.16.

Documentation

The quality manual should have a section dedicated to document and data control. It should contain policies committing the company to comply with the nine requirements of this section; a short outline procedure explaining how the requirements are implemented; and references to the operational procedures that apply. The manual should also contain a list of the types of documents that are controlled in compliance with this section (see the following Section 4.5.1).

In small companies it may be sufficient to have only one operational procedure regulating the entire document control system. In larger companies it is usual to have separate procedures for control of different types of documents, since they are issued by different departments and may be controlled in different ways. There is no merit in trying to standardize the document control system for all types of documents. While all requirements in this section must be implemented for all types of documents, the methods and degree of control should be adopted to reflect the relative importance of documents and the environment in which they are transmitted and used.

In addition to the operational procedures dedicated to document control, every procedure dealing with activities that may involve issuing of documents (for example, design, production control, or process control), should prescribe particular rules for review and approval of these specific documents.

4.5.1   General

Requirement

Define the document control system and the types of controlled documents.

The structure of the document control system should be well explained, so that it is clear who is responsible for controlling different types of documents. It is especially important in organizations where the document control system is not centralized and where each department issues and controls its own documents. It must be also clear which types, or categories, of documents are controlled.

The following categories of documents must be controlled to comply with QS-9000:

- **Quality system documentation** — quality manual and operational procedures.

- **Inspection and testing procedures** — control plans, process control procedures, inspection and testing instructions, etc.

- **Job instructions** — specific work or task instructions and checklists, including: process procedures, setup instructions, handling procedures, equipment operating manuals, training instructions, etc.

- **Engineering documentation** — drawings, specifications, bills of materials, parts lists, math data, acceptance criteria, workmanship standards, etc.

- **Standards** — international, national, industrial, and proprietary standards and codes.

The control requirements apply equally to documents and data stored in electronic media, such as computer files, databases, and so forth.

Procedures

General presentation of the document control system can be included in the quality manual or, in larger organizations, in a separate operational procedure (there is such procedure in the *QS-9000 Documentation* software). The categories of controlled documents are usually defined in the quality manual. Procedures explaining how to control specific types of documents should also name the categories of documents to which they pertain.

Records

The evidence of compliance is a list specifying the types of controlled documents. The list can be included in the quality manual or a procedure.

Audit

Auditors will verify that all relevant documents are included in the document control system. Everyone remembers to control the quality manual, operational procedures, and engineering documents, but people often forget to include in the document control system such documents as setup instructions, training instructions, equipment maintenance plans, or packaging specifications.

4.5.2   Document and Data Approval and Issue

Requirement

Review and approve documents prior to issue.

Every document must bear a signature(s), or other identification, of the authorized personnel who reviewed and approved the document. If more than one signature is on a document, it should be clear which signatures evidence review and which evidence approval. The approval signature usually distinguishes an issued document from its draft or preliminary versions. For each type of document, the authority to approve and issue documents must be defined.

82   **QS-9000 REQUIREMENTS**

Procedures

The general document control procedure, or specific procedures for various types of documents, should have a section dealing specifically with review and approval of documents. The procedure(s) should explain the manner and scope of review, and define the level of authority required to approve and issue various types of documents.

Records

Signatures on documents provide the required record and sufficient evidence of compliance. For documents in electronic media, the signatures may be substituted by initials or other identification of those who reviewed and approved the documents.

Audit

Compliance is checked not only in the locations where documents are issued and controlled, but also everywhere else where they are used and stored. When examining documents, auditors always look for review and approval status. It is a reflex.

Requirement

Identify documents with their revision level, and maintain a master list with current revision status of documents.

Documents should be directly identified with their revision level. Consecutive numbering using numerals or letters is the most common method, but in some cases it may be appropriate to include the revision level in the code identifying a document, or simply use the date of issue as indication of the revision level.

There must also be a system for verifying what is the current revision level of a given document. The most common method is a master list of issued documents. To satisfy this requirement, the list need only specify the latest revision of a document; however, it could also contain additional information, such as the date of issue, identification of the issuing authority, and distribution of the document. This would also help to comply with other document control requirements. Document master lists can be maintained on computer databases, catalog cards, or manual logs.

Procedures

The general document control procedure should have a section dealing with identification and verification of document revision status. The procedure should instruct how revision levels are identified for various types of documents, and prescribe specific means for recording their revision status.

Records

Records and evidence of compliance are provided by the documents themselves, displaying their revision level (or date of issue); and by master lists providing the means for verifying the current revision status of documents.

Audit

Assessing compliance, auditors will check if documents display their revision levels, and will review the master lists or logs of issued documents. Auditors will also test the system for verifying revision status. They will pick a sample of documents (from different locations around the company), note their revision levels, and ask for the verification that these revision levels are indeed the last issued.

Requirement

Ensure that current documents are available at all locations where they are needed.

There are two issues in this requirement. One is identification of the locations where specific documents should be available, and the other is effective distribution of the documents. For documents having permanent or fairly constant distribution, there should be documented distribution lists. The lists can be printed on the documents themselves or be maintained separately.

When distribution cannot be predicted in advance, documents can be made available on an as-needed basis. But their use must be recorded so that it is known where to follow up with revisions. If maintaining such a record is not practical, documents should be destroyed promptly or returned after one-time use. Any filing or storage of documents that cannot be automatically replaced with new revisions must be prohibited.

84   QS-9000 REQUIREMENTS

Procedures

The general document control procedure, or specific procedures dealing with various types of documents, should have a section dedicated to distribution of documents. The procedure(s) should explain how distribution lists are documented and maintained, and what means are used to physically deliver documents to their destinations. They should also explain, if applicable, how to use letters of transmittal, sign-off logs, or other means for confirmation of receipt. This procedure can be combined with the procedure regulating withdrawal of obsolete documents from points of use (see next requirement).

Records

Distribution lists are the main evidence that the locations where documents should be placed are identified. The actual distribution of documents can be recorded in letters of transmittal, distribution logs, or simply by checking off a distribution list. Any method is acceptable as long as it is documented in procedures. Establishment and maintenance of receipt records is not explicitly required.

Audit

Assessing compliance, auditors will review the distribution lists and records, and test the distribution system. This can be done by either picking a name from a distribution list and verifying that the person indeed has the document; or the other way around, by picking up a document from somebody's file and verifying that the person is on the document's distribution list.

Requirement

Remove obsolete documents from points of use and identify retained historical copies of obsolete documents to preclude unintended use.

Obsolete documents are usually removed from points of use at the same time that new revisions of the documents are distributed. There are basically two possibilities. Either superseded documents are exchanged for revised versions, or the recipients of revised documents are obliged to destroy the old copies. Direct exchange is more effective, of course, but the other system is also acceptable, provided that it can be satisfactorily implemented.

When historical documents need to be retained for preservation of knowledge and/or legal reasons, they should be stamped OBSOLETE or HISTORY, and be kept separate from current documents to preclude unintended use.

Procedures

The general document control procedure, or specific procedures dealing with various types of documents, should have a section dedicated to withdrawal and handling of obsolete documents. The procedure(s) should explain the method used for withdrawal of obsolete documents, and prohibit unauthorized filing and storage of any obsolete documents and any documents that are at risk of becoming obsolete because they are not automatically updated with new revisions. The procedure should also explain how historical copies of obsolete documents are identified and stored.

Records

There are normally no records or other written evidence that obsolete documents are being withdrawn from points of use, unless a document exchange system involves logging the withdrawn documents. Handling and storage of historical copies of obsolete documents is evidenced by proper identification of the documents themselves.

Audit

Because there are generally no records or other written evidence, the compliance will be assessed by auditing and testing the system. Auditors will check documents against their master lists and will look out for multiple revisions of a document in files and points of use. They will also review the files of obsolete historical documents.

4.5.2.1　Engineering Specifications

Requirement

Control customer engineering documents and maintain a records of their implementation in production.

This automotive requirement calls for a procedure for review, distribution, and implementation of customer engineering documents. There is really nothing new in this requirement. The original ISO 9000 standard recognizes that customer engineering documents must be controlled. In consequence, all requirements of this Section 4.5 must be implemented with regard to customer engineering documents, except for those pertaining to approval and issue of documents (they are issued by customers).

This subsection is also concerned with the timeliness of the review and implementation of customer documentation and changes; and requires that the date on which each change is implemented in production be recorded.

The NOTE in this subsection reminds that specification changes may require updating of the PPAP documents.

Procedures

The procedure for controlling customer engineering documents should instruct how the receipt of these documents is logged (possibly with confirmation of receipt), who reviews them before distribution and how many days are allowed for the review, how distribution and implementation dates are recorded, and how obsolete documents are withdrawn from points of use. There should also be a list, or other means, to verify that all implemented document are on the latest revision level.

Records

Records and evidence of compliance are document transmittal letters, logs, review records, distribution lists, and master lists with latest revision levels.

Audit

Auditors will review relevant records, and will audit files and work areas to verify that all engineering documents are properly distributed, and that only latest revisions are used. Auditors will also verify the timeliness of the review and implementation of customer's engineering specifications, and will check whether appropriate PPAP documents have been updated in response to changed specifications.

4.5.3   Document and Data Changes

Requirement

Review and approve changes in documents and reissues of revised documents.

Review and approval of revisions involving reissue of a document on a higher revision level should follow the same procedure that applies to issuing initial documents (refer to the first requirement in this section).

Corrections in documents, often called red-line corrections, must also be reviewed and approved. Anything crossed out, added, or changed in a controlled document is a noncompliance unless the change is signed by an authorized person. Red-line corrections should not be left on documents indefinitely. Documents should be reissued after a practical number of changes have been made.

Handwritten notes and comments on documents should be avoided. Even though they do not modify the original content of a document, they add new information that is not authorized and will be lost when the document is reissued and the marked-up copy destroyed.

Procedures

The procedure dealing with document changes should define the channels for requesting changes in documents; provide rules for making corrections in documents, including their review and approval; and instruct how documents should be reissued on a higher revision level.

Records

Records and evidence of compliance are the signatures authorizing corrections and reissues of revised documents.

Audit

Any handwritten corrections and notes on documents will alert auditors and provoke questioning. Signed-off corrections are acceptable, but the sign-offs must be authorized and all concerned functions must be notified about the correction.

Requirement

At distribution, highlight changes in revised documents.

It cannot be assumed that recipients of revised documents engage in a systematic comparative analysis of the new and the old documents to detect the changes. The standard requires, therefore, that the changes be identified. The most common way to identify changes is to summarize them on distribution cover sheets or transmittal letters, if used. Less formal methods — for example, highlighting, marking on margins, or identifying changes on self-stick notes — are also acceptable, provided these methods are documented in procedures, and thus are officially sanctioned.

Procedures

The procedure regulating distribution of revised documents should prescribe specific methods for highlighting changes in revised documents.

Records

Records and evidence of compliance are the distribution cover sheets that accompany revised documents, or the documents themselves, if they are marked to highlight the changes.

Audit

Assessing compliance, auditors will review the cover sheets, transmittal letters, and other evidence of compliance; and will interview recipients of documents, asking how they are informed about specific changes that have been made in the revised documents they receive.

* * * * *

Further reading

- Standard ISO 9004 Part 1, Sect. 5.3 and Sect.17
- J. Kanholm, *ISO 9000 Quality System*, Chap. 15
- J. Kanholm, *QS-9000 Documentation*: QM Sect. 5 and Operational Procedures QOP-05-01 and QOP-05-02

PURCHASING

4.6 Purchasing

Application

Requirements of this section apply to purchased products that are intended for incorporation into the final product, and associated services, such as heat treating, painting, plating, etc.

Documentation

The quality manual should have a section dedicated to purchasing. It should contain policies committing the company to comply with the eight requirements discussed below; a short outline procedure explaining how the requirements are implemented; and references to the operational procedures that apply.

There must also be an operational procedure dealing with the purchasing activities. In companies where different functions are responsible for selection of subcontractors and establishment of purchasing documents, these activities should be documented in separate procedures. Also, if controls applied to purchasing of standard catalog products are significantly different from those applied to the purchasing of custom products, it may be better to have a separate procedure for each category.

4.6.1 General

4.6.1.1 Approved Materials for Ongoing Production

Requirement

When required, use customer-designated subcontractors.

When so required by contract or indicated in specifications or drawings, suppliers may only use subcontractors that are approved or designated by customers. The use of customer-designated subcontractors does not relieve suppliers from the responsibility of ensuring quality and on-time delivery. Suppliers should therefore prequalify subcontractors and monitor their quality performance, even though the subcontractors are designated by customers. If a customer-designated subcontractor does not meet quality capability requirements, or is otherwise unacceptable, the supplier should request the customer to approve alternative subcontractors.

Procedures

A procedure and/or quality manual should clearly state the policy that, when required by the customer, the company will use only customer-designated or customer-approved subcontractors. The procedure should also instruct buyers to request customer approval of additional subcontractors when the initially designated subcontractor is not acceptable.

Records

Records evidencing compliance with this requirement are company's approved subcontractor lists and purchase orders. Also relevant are customer lists approved suppliers and subcontractors.

Audit

Auditors will review the approved subcontractor list and verify that, when required, all subcontractors have been also approved by the customer (or that they are the same as designated in customer lists or specifications).

4.6.1.2   Government, Safety and Environmental Regulations

Requirement

Ensure that purchased products satisfy safety, environmental, and other governmental regulations.

This requirement expresses the concern of OEM customers that materials used in the supplied products comply with all governmental safety, environmental, electrical, and electromagnetic regulations of the countries where products are manufactured and sold. To satisfy this requirement suppliers should have a system for identifying which materials and products are regulated, and for ensuring that the applicable regulations are complied with. A practical system can be based on requesting subcontractors to identify restricted, hazardous, and otherwise regulated materials, and to warrant that the supplied materials comply with all applicable regulations. Such request should be included in subcontracts and purchase orders.

Procedures

Appropriate purchasing procedure should instruct that whenever there is a reason to believe that the purchased products may be restricted or regulated, purchase orders should request subcontractors to warrant compliance of their products with applicable governmental regulations. Those reviewing and approving purchase orders should also be instructed to verify that indeed such requests are included when appropriate.

Records

Evidence of compliance consists of certificates, warrants, labels, reports, etc., demonstrating that purchased products comply with applicable governmental regulations.

Audit

Assessing compliance, auditors will ask how purchasing knows which materials may be restricted, hazardous, or otherwise regulated, and how they ensure that such materials comply with applicable governmental regulations. Auditors will also ask which specific materials used in production fall into this category, and will review the evidence that these materials comply with regulations.

4.6.2   Evaluation of Subcontractors

Requirement

Evaluate subcontractors, monitor their quality performance, and maintain records of their quality capabilities and performance.

Regardless whether subcontractors are selected by the supplier or are designated by customers, all subcontractors should be evaluated to determine their ability to meet subcontract requirements, including quality requirements. The scope and depth of the evaluation can vary, depending on the criticallity and complexity of the subcontracted products, and the knowledge of and experience with the subcontractor. Typically the evaluation will include reviewing references, investigating the subcontractor's process capabilities, and auditing their quality system. Only those subcontractors who pass the initial evaluation (or prequalification) may be used. Those subcontractors that have been used for some time prior to implementation of QS-9000 may be exempted from this requirement for initial evaluation (i.e., can be grandfathered).

All subcontractors must be continuously monitored with regard to their quality performance. Quality problems should be recorded and brought to the attention of the subcontractors. They should be requested to propose and implement corrective actions to address their problems. When appropriate, the monitoring system should also include quality system audits, process capability verifications, and source inspections.

The system for prequalifying and monitoring subcontractors requires collecting and analyzing documents and records that provide information about the subcontractors capabilities and performance. These can be references, process capability and audit reports, product nonconformance records, corrective action requests, and so forth. These documents should be properly organized and maintained. This is usually done by having a separate quality record file for each subcontractor. The subcontractor quality records should be reviewed regularly, and the conclusions utilized for making decisions regarding their approval status.

Procedures   The operational procedure for evaluation, approval, and monitoring of subcontractors should assign the responsibility for conducting the evaluations; provide guidelines for determining their scope; outline the elements and scope of the system for monitoring subcontractor's

　　QS-9000 REQUIREMENTS　　93

quality performance; and define how the quality assurance and purchasing departments should cooperate and interface in operating the system. If subcontractors are regularly audited, there should also be a procedure explaining how to initiate, conduct, and report subcontractor quality system audits, including audit checklists (the procedure can be combined with internal audit procedures).

The system for collecting and analyzing subcontractor quality records should be also documented in a procedure. The procedure should explain what kinds of records are collected; who reviews the records and how often; and how the subcontractor approval status is recorded and communicated to other concerned functions.

Records

The evidence of compliance consists of the subcontractor quality record files, which contain records of their quality capabilities and performance histories. There should also be evidence that the records are regularly reviewed and the information is used in selecting subcontractors.

Audit

Assessing compliance, auditors will verify that all relevant subcontractors and suppliers are prequalified before they receive purchasing contracts, and that their quality performance is being regularly monitored. Auditors will also review the content of the subcontractor quality record files, verifying that the files are maintained; that recorded quality problems are communicated back to the subcontractors; and that they implement corrective actions to address the identified problems.

Requirement

Maintain a list of approved subcontractors.

All functions involved with specifying, requisitioning, and purchasing materials and products should have current information with regard to approval status of subcontractors. This is usually achieved by maintaining and distributing an approved subcontractor list. The list can be maintained on computer and be distributed on-line, or be printed out. The list must be a controlled document.

A new NOTE in this section reminds that the actual list of approved subcontractors is not explicitly required in the standard. Rather, the requirement is that the status of subcontractor approval must be recorded and must be communicated to all personnel who are involved in purchasing decisions. A list is the most common way to satisfy this requirement, but any alternative methods are also acceptable.

Procedures

Appropriate procedure should assign the responsibility for establishing and maintaining the approved subcontractor list, specify how often the list should be updated, and explain who should use the list and how.

Records

Records of compliance with this requirement are the approved subcontractor list, subcontractor qualification records and, when required, records evidencing customer approval of subcontractors.

Audit

Auditors will review the approved subcontractor list and subcontractor qualification and quality performance records to verify that only subcontractors who have been properly evaluated and who perform satisfactorily are included on the list. Auditors will also review a sample of purchase orders, noting whether the subcontractors actually used are on the list and have been approved.

4.6.2.1   Subcontractor Development

Requirement

Perform subcontractor quality system development with the goal of subcontractor compliance to QS-9000.

While full and immediate compliance with QS-9000 is not yet required of subcontractors, the third edition of the standard has taken definitive steps in this direction. While the second edition required more general development of the awareness of subcontractors, the third edition states clearly that the ultimate goal is full compliance with the whole Section I of QS-9000.

This requirement obliges suppliers to work with (develop) subcontractors toward implementation of a QS-9000 quality system. Suppliers should foster a quality partnership with their subcontractors, including involvement of subcontractors in quality planning activities, sharing quality performance data, assessing subcontractors quality systems, and so forth. Passing PPAP requirements on to subcontractors could be the focal point for subcontractor development. This would be a natural starting point, as a subcontractor part approval process must be established anyway in response to requirements of QS-9000 Section 4.2.4.2

If QS-9000 capability of a subcontractor is to be recognized and their QS-9000 status used in determining the amount of receiving inspection, for example, the subcontractor must be regularly audited by the supplier, the OEM customer, or an accredited third-party registrar.

Procedures

The procedure dealing with subcontractor evaluation and monitoring should outline a program for QS-9000 development of subcontractors, and assign the responsibility for carrying it out. The procedure may also prescribe a system for monitoring subcontractor progress toward achieving QS-9000 capability.

Records

At a minimum, records and evidence of compliance should consist of letters, memoranda, or minutes of meetings demonstrating that subcontractors are made aware of QS-9000 and are being encouraged to implement a QS-9000 quality system. In addition there should be records of specific activities and their results. (For example, copies of subcontractor QS-9000 registration certificates, subcontractor audit reports, or records demonstrating that subcontractors are involved in quality planning.)

Audit

Auditors will go through the approved subcontractor list and ask how specific subcontractors are being developed using QS-9000. Auditors will expect the most important subcontractors to be committed to, and be advancing toward, full compliance with all fundamental requirements of the standard.

4.6.2.2   Scheduling Subcontractors

Requirement

Require on-time delivery from subcontractors and monitor their delivery performance.

This section of the standard obliges suppliers to require 100 percent on-time delivery performance of their subcontractors; to have a system for tracking the delivery performance; to provide subcontractors with long-term planning information to help them achieve the required performance; and to maintain records of premium freight, whether paid by the supplier or the subcontractor.

This requirement will not be satisfied if purchase orders do not specify requested delivery dates. Such delivery time designations as "ASAP" or "Soonest" are not acceptable. On-time delivery performance can be tracked by recording the actual delivery dates and comparing them with the requested dates. This can be done in a special data base, or in connection with processing and recording of other delivery information. At a minimum, the system should be capable of identifying and recording all late deliveries and premium freight charges. Subcontractors with poor delivery performance should be required to implement corrective actions to address the underlying problems.

Procedures

Appropriate operational procedure should require that specific delivery dates be requested in contracts and purchase orders, and should explain the system for tracking delivery performance of subcontractors. There should also be a link with the Corrective and Preventive Action procedure, to be used with subcontractors that repeatedly fail to deliver on time. The requirement for providing subcontractors with advance planning information and purchasing commitments need only be addressed in the quality manual as a general policy.

Records

The record and evidence of compliance consist of purchase orders and reports of subcontractor delivery performance. Additional records are corrective action requests and other evidence that unsatisfactory on-time delivery performance is not tolerated and provokes appropriate response actions.

Audit

Auditors will check purchasing documents to verify that specific delivery dates are requested, and will review records of subcontractors on-time delivery performance. Auditors will also ask for evidence that appropriate actions are initiated in response to late deliveries. Compliance with the requirement for providing subcontractors with advance planning information and purchasing commitments is difficult to audit, and will not be questioned unless there is evidence, or even suspicion, that poor delivery performance of a subcontractor is indeed caused by unrealistically short lead times.

4.6.3   Purchasing Data

Requirement

Precisely and completely describe the ordered products, and review and approve purchasing documents prior to release.

Section 4.6.3 provides a detailed list of the kinds of features and characteristics that should be used to describe products in purchase orders and contracts. There is really no need for interpretation — the list is self-explanatory.

The review and approval of purchasing documents should ensure that the subcontractor is approved; that the products are adequately defined; that all relevant quality requirements are stated; that restricted or otherwise regulated substances comply with governmental regulations; and that packaging and delivery requirements, including requested delivery dates, are clearly specified. The review should be evidenced by a record, which can simply be an approval signature.

Procedures

The procedure for establishing purchasing documents should assign the responsibility and authority for review and approval of purchasing documents, and outline the scope of the review. It should also specify what constitutes the record of review and how to distinguish approved documents. In addition, the procedure should provide a list of product features and characteristics that may be relevant when specifying products. The list will be similar to that included in QS-9000 Section 4.6.3. The list and an explanation of how to use it can be also issued as job instruction.

Records

Usually, the only records and evidence of implementation are the approval signatures on purchasing documents, unless the system also requires establishment of other records.

Audit

Assessing compliance, auditors will review a sample of purchase orders, checking how products are described and if the documents are approved. They may also interview personnel who prepare purchasing documents and those who review them, to verify that they know and use the procedures relevant to these activities. Common omissions in purchase orders are imprecise description of ordered products, lack of revision level identification for drawings, and lack of requests for material certificates and testing reports.

4.6.4   Verification of Purchased Product

4.6.4.1   Supplier Verification at Subcontractor's Premises

4.6.4.2   Customer Verification of Subcontracted Product

Requirement

When appropriate, verify purchased products at subcontractor's premises and afford the same right to your customers.

Procedures

The first part of this requirement, corresponding to Section 4.6.4.1, can be complied with by including in the purchasing procedure a policy stating that if purchased products are to be verified at subcontractor's premises, appropriate arrangements and the method of product release should be specified in purchasing documents.

The second part of the requirement, corresponding to Section 4.6.4.2, can be documented in the quality manual. The manual should contain a policy committing the company to afford its customers the right to verify purchased products at source; and state that customer verification does not absolve the company from the responsibility to supply acceptable product.

Records

There is normally no records other than contracts that contain provisions for source inspections.

Audit

Assessing compliance, auditors will inquire whether there were any cases of source inspections and will ask for the corresponding contracts to verify that appropriate arrangements and methods of product release are specified.

* * * * *

Further reading

- Standard ISO 9004 Part 1, Sect. 9

- J. Kanholm, *ISO 9000 Quality System*, Chap. 7

- J. Kanholm, *QS-9000 Documentation*: QM Sect. 6 and Operational Procedures OOP-06-01 and OOP-06-02

CONTROL OF CUSTOMER SUPPLIED PRODUCT

4.7 Control of Customer Supplied Product

4.7.1 Customer Owned Tooling

Application

This section applies to materials and components supplied by customers for incorporation into the final product, and to customer owned tooling, test equipment, returnable packaging, and other such equipment and supplies. If your company does not receive from its customers any products or equipment, this section does not apply.

Documentation

If the section does not apply, the quality manual should state so and explain why, and nothing more need be done. Otherwise, the manual should contain a policy committing the company to comply with the requirement discussed below; provide a short outline procedure explaining how the requirement is implemented; and reference the operational procedures that apply. In cases where handling of customer supplied products follows rules similar to those that apply to purchased products, there is no need for establishing new operational procedures.

Requirement

Establish procedures for verification, storage, and maintenance of customer supplied products and customer owned equipment.

QS-9000 does not prescribe any specific requirements for verification, storage, and protection of customer supplied products or customer owned equipment. It only requires that there be documented procedures for these activities. In most situations, the same procedures that are used for verification, storage, and protection of purchased products and company owned equipment can be applied directly to customer products.

There is also a requirement to notify customers in the event of damage or loss of their products.

Section 4.7.1 requires that customer owned tooling and equipment must be permanently marked with identification of ownership.

Procedures

Although the requirement calls for documented procedures, in most cases there is no need to write new procedures. If customer products and equipment are treated in the same way as purchased products and company owned equipment, the quality manual should state so and, on procedure level, the application of relevant existing procedures should be expanded to include customer products and equipment. The manual and/or procedures should also instruct that any event of damage or loss of customer's products and equipment be reported back to the customer, and that customer's tooling and equipment should be marked with identification of ownership.

Records

Records and evidence of compliance are of the same type as those that apply to verification, storage, and handling of purchased products and company owned equipment. In addition, there may also be reports informing customers of unsuitability, damage, or loss of their products.

Audit

Assessing compliance, auditors will review procedures for verification, storage, maintenance and marking of customer supplied products and customer owned equipment, and will verify that these procedures are effectively implemented. Auditors will expect that customer products and equipment are controlled on at least the same level as purchased products and company owned equipment.

* * * * *

Further reading

- Standard ISO 9004 Part 1, Sect. 9
- J. Kanholm, *ISO 9000 Quality System*, Chap. 7
- J. Kanholm, *QS-9000 Documentation*, QM Sect. 7, and Operational Procedure MOP-07-01

8 PRODUCT IDENTIFICATION AND TRACEABILITY

4.8 Product Identification and Traceability

Application

Product identification requirements apply to materials, components, and subassemblies intended for incorporation into the final product, and to the final products themselves. Product identification should be maintained from receipt and during all stages of production, delivery, and installation. The manner of identifying final products is usually specified by customers. Traceability requirements apply only when traceability is required by regulations, is specified in a contract or when the company maintains a voluntary traceability system.

Documentation

The quality manual should have a section dedicated to product identification and traceability. It should contain policies committing the company to identify products and, when applicable, maintain traceability systems; a short outline procedure explaining how these policies are implemented; and references to the operational procedures that apply.

There must also be an operational procedure explaining the product identification system and, if traceability is required, another procedure dealing with traceability.

Requirement

Identify materials, components, and products during all stages of production.

Products are usually identified by part numbers or, when generic materials are involved, by their trade names. The identification numbers and names should be the same as those used in drawings, bills of materials, work orders, and other documentation defining the products and methods of production. Customers often specify the required product identification, especially for final products.

Materials and components are normally identified using markings, tags, or labels applied directly to the products or to their packaging or containers. Subassemblies and products moving through production processes can be identified by production work orders or travelers (also called shop tickets, flow tags, routing cards, etc.) that are kept together with the products. Identification of final products is usually specified by the customer and is defined in product drawings and specifications.

Product identification should be maintained throughout all stages of receiving, storage, production, and delivery. All products at all stages must be identified, without exceptions.

Procedures

The operational procedure for identifying materials, components, and products should explain how part numbers are generated and who is responsible for their assignment; how assignment of part numbers is recorded; and what means are used for identifying different categories of products and who is responsible for applying the identification. The procedure should also instruct all personnel to protect and maintain the markings, tags, and labels that identify products.

Job instructions may be required when the identification system is complex and needs to be explained in detail, beyond what can be done in an operational procedure. Also, complex methods for product marking may require written instructions.

Records

Records and evidence of compliance consist of bills of materials, parts lists, catalogs, and other documentation and records of assigned part numbers; and the tags, labels, and markings identifying products.

Audit

Assessing compliance, auditors will review the system of assigning, documenting, and recording part numbers, paying special attention to parts lists. The lists are considered controlled documents and must be established and maintained in compliance with requirements of Section 5, Document and Data Control. On the implementation level, auditors will verify that all materials, components, and products are identified at all stages of production.

Requirement

If required, develop procedures for unique identification of individual products and batches to ensure traceability.

As stated in the introduction, QS-9000 Section 4.8 does not in itself require traceability for any categories of products. This section requires that, when a traceability system is maintained for any reason, it must be documented in procedures.

Traceability is usually specified by customers or governmental regulations, or it can be implemented voluntarily to help with managing quality and servicing. Each automotive customer has special traceability requirements. They are referenced in QS-9000 Section II, Customer-specific Requirements.

Procedures

Traceability should be documented on two levels: product level and system level. On the product level there should be a traceability plan for each product type. It should clearly specify which materials, components, operations, and processes must be traceable; what information should be collected for each traceable element; how the traceability information should be recorded; and how the traceability records should be maintained and for how long. The plan does not have to be issued as a special independent document. Traceability requirements can be defined in many different documents, such as drawings, specifications, procedures, etc.

On the system level there should be an operational procedure explaining how traceability plans are established, issued and used (or which documents specify traceability requirements); how to assign serial or batch numbers or other unique identification, and who is responsible for doing it; how to establish and correlate traceability records; what measures should be employed to safeguard against loss of traceability; and what should be done when traceability is lost at any stage.

Job instructions may be required when the traceability system is complex and needs to be explained in detail, beyond what can be done in an operational procedure and/or by referencing customer documents. Also, complex methods for product marking may require written instructions.

Records

Records and evidence of compliance consist of the traceability plans, serial or batch number records, and other traceability records. Markings, tags, and labels used for unique identification of products are also part of the evidence.

Audit

Assessing compliance, auditors will review the traceability plans and verify that they are authorized and are available in receiving, storage, and production areas. They will also review the traceability records, paying special attention to the completeness of the records and compliance with traceability plans.

On the implementation level, auditors will verify that the traceable materials and components are adequately identified, and will assess whether measures employed to safeguard against loss of traceability are effectively implemented.

* * * * *

Further reading

- Standard ISO 9004 Part 1, Sect. 11.2

- J. Kanholm, *ISO 9000 Quality System*, Chap. 10

- J. Kanholm, *QS-9000 Documentation*, QM Sect. 8, and Operational Procedure OOP-08-01

PROCESS CONTROL

4.9

Application

Process Control

This section applies to any process that directly affects product quality. Under such broad definition, the application of this section comprises production, assembly, storage, packaging, and delivery processes. But in practice, the requirements are mostly applicable to production and assembly.

Documentation

The quality manual should have a section dedicated to process control. It should contain policies committing the company to comply with all requirements of this section; a short outline procedure explaining how the policies are implemented; and references to the operational procedures that apply.

In small companies it may be sufficient to have only one operational procedure addressing all requirements. But to do it well, there should really be at least four procedures: for production planning and scheduling, for process operator instructions, for process control, and for preventive maintenance. Although included in the same QS-9000 section, the requirements corresponding to these four procedures have very little in common and each needs to be addressed by an independent system.

Note

The original ISO 9000 text in this section includes a broad, catch-all requirement that production processes be planned and be carried out under controlled conditions, and a list specifying seven process control elements that must be implemented to achieve these conditions. However, the supplemental automotive requirements and notes added to this section render the original ISO 9000 text largely irrelevant. Except for the requirement to plan production processes, the supplemental automotive sections restate and expand every other requirement of ISO 9000.

For this reason, only the first requirement in this section, for planning production processes, has its origin in ISO 9000. All remaining requirements correspond to the supplemental automotive sections.

Requirement

Plan production activities and processes.

Production process planning is usually carried out concurrently with quality planning. There can be no meaningful quality plan when it is not known which processes will be used in production. The same documents that are established in the course of quality planning can be used to demonstrate compliance with the present requirement for production process planning. These documents may be floor plan layouts, production and process flowcharts, process FMEAs, production work orders, travelers, and so forth. In fact, any document, or a set of documents, that specifies and sequences production activities and processes can be considered a production process plan. The production process plan should be included in the process monitoring and operator instructions (see the requirement of Section 4.9.1).

Procedures

The production process planning activity is usually documented in the same procedure that deals with production planning/scheduling (establishing production work orders, travelers, etc.). As an alternative, production process planning can be addressed in the procedure dealing with quality planning, as these activities are concurrent and intertwining. Either procedure should have a subsection dedicated to production process planning, where it should explain who is responsible for the planning, and how the plan is documented and communicated.

Records

Production plans themselves, whether they are flow charts, production work orders, or other such documents, provide the evidence of compliance.

Audit

Assessing compliance, auditors will review the production process plans and verify that they indeed cover all production steps. Preparation of materials, such as cutting, cleaning, painting, etc., and the subcontracted operations, should be included. Auditors will also note if the plans have been reviewed and approved prior to release and otherwise satisfy document control requirements.

4.9.b.1   Cleanliness of Premises

Requirement

Ensure that premises are maintained in a state of order, cleanliness and repair.

In addition to the general requirement in ISO 9000 calling for a "suitable working environment," the third edition of QS-9000 added a subsection dealing with cleanliness of premises. Together, these requirements relate to housekeeping, cleanliness, lighting, noise, ventilation, air conditioning, and facility maintenance. Conditions that may trigger a noncompliance are, for example: dust, dirt and accumulation of scrap; overcrowding, poor lighting, excessive noise, or inadequate ventilation; equipment parts, tools and supplies scattered around and/or intermingled with production materials and components; accumulation of unused, downgraded or scrapped materials around machines and work stations; obstructed transportation or fire lanes; leaking roofs, broken windows and other signs of building disrepair; and so forth.

Procedures

The commitments to establish and maintain premises in a state of cleanliness and to provide suitable working environment are usually documented in the quality manual without the need for a special operational procedure.

Records

There are usually no records demonstrating cleanliness and suitable work environment, although some companies keep cleaning and facility maintenance records, especially when these activities are subcontracted.

Audit

In most cases the audit will be limited to observation of the production areas. Auditors will pay attention to such conditions as overcrowding, accumulation of dirt and unused or scrapped material, leaking roofs, broken windows, and so forth. Because of the subjective nature of this requirement, auditors will probably hold back their judgement and write formal noncompliances only in extreme situations or when there are known complaints or quality problems related to housekeeping and working environment.

4.9.b.2   Contingency Plans

Requirement

Prepare contingency plans to protect supply of product in the event of emergency.

This is a new requirement added in the third edition of QS-9000. It obliges suppliers to protect customers from interruptions of product supply in the event of foreseeable emergencies. The plans should identify foreseeable emergencies relevant to such aspects as plant location and type, raw materials and component supplies, local labor market, history of utility interruptions, and the reliability and the consequences of key equipment breakdown. For each identified emergency, the plan should evaluate the impact on the customer's supply of product and define measures to mitigate or minimize these impacts. These measures may include alternative transportation of materials or products, emergency power generating, provisions for hiring out-of-area temporary labor, maintenance of replacement parts and subassemblies for key equipment, supply of products from another plant, and so forth.

Procedures

While the contingency plans do not need to be issued as a separate and dedicated document, all elements of the plans must be somehow documented. For example, Human Resources can establish plans regarding labor shortages, Purchasing regarding alternative suppliers and/or transportation carriers, and Maintenance regarding emergency repair or replacement of key equipment.

In most companies the policies and responsibilities regarding contingency planning can be documented in the quality manual alone, without the need for an independent operational procedure. In addition, procedures pertaining to production planning, facility and equipment maintenance and other relevant procedures may have sections supporting contingency planning. The manual and procedures should assign the responsibilities for identifying and planning for potential contingencies and instruct on how to document the plans.

Records

Records and evidence of compliance are the contingency plans, whether issued as a separate and independent document, or as departmental policies, procedures, memos, checklists or other such documents. Where contingency plans have been implemented in the past, there should also be records of their implementation.

Audit

Auditors will be looking for clear policy statements and procedures instructing in the establishment of contingency planning to protect customer's supply of product, and will ask for specific contingency plans. While the standard does not define the scope and extent of contingency planning, auditors will expect to see some specific and meaningful plans in at least those areas where there is a history of previous emergencies. Direct questioning regarding past emergencies and review of delivery records will point auditors to the relevant issues.

4.9.d.1   Designation of Special Characteristics

This section is just a reminder that suppliers shall comply with all customer requirements regarding Special Characteristics. These requirements are defined in QS-9000 Section I and II and in the PPAP reference manual. This section also reminds that suppliers must maintain appropriate documents and records to demonstrate that they comply with Special Characteristics requirements.

4.9.g.1   Preventive Maintenance

Requirement

Develop planned, comprehensive maintenance plan for process equipment and machines.

Any acceptable system for maintenance of production equipment must focus on prevention. Repairing breakdowns is not enough to comply. There should be a preventive maintenance plan for each machine, and records evidencing that the plan is implemented. The maintenance plan can be a list or matrix specifying how often fluids, filters, seals, drive belts, and other parts and supplies need to be inspected and/or changed. Equipment manufacturer's maintenance manuals should be available and be used when establishing the maintenance plan. Other input into the maintenance plan should include information on such items as tool wear, optimization of uptime, process performance (SPC) data, important characteristics of perishable tooling, fluid analysis, infrared monitoring of circuits, vibration analysis, and so forth.

Procedures

A procedure describing planned maintenance activities and a specific maintenance schedule are explicitly required in the standard. The procedure should instruct how to prepare the maintenance plan and schedule; what are the servicing verification requirements; how maintenance records should be established; how maintenance activities should be recorded in process control (SPC) charts; and it should assign specific responsibilities for these activities.

Job instructions may be required for performing various maintenance activities and repairs. If equipment manufacturers manuals provide adequate maintenance instructions, there is no need for additional, in-house issued instructions.

Records

Records and evidence of compliance consist of equipment maintenance plans, schedules and and records.

Audit

Assessing compliance, auditors will review the equipment maintenance plans, noting if all relevant machines are included and if the plans are consistent with equipment manufacturer's recommendations; and will review the maintenance records to verify that the plans are consistently implemented. Auditors will also review machine downtime statistics, SPC charts and other relevant records to evaluate whether the preventive maintenance plan is effective.

Requirement

Maintain, or have access to, replacement parts for key manufacturing equipment.

Suppliers must establish requirements for, and ensure availability of, replacement parts for key manufacturing equipment. This is usually satisfied by establishing a list of critical parts that are either maintained in stock or can be delivered on short notice from a distributor. For those parts that are maintained in stock, there should be a system for recording the location of each part, and the current stock level. For parts that are available from distributors or equipment manufacturers, there should be documented information on where and how to order the part, how long does it take to receive the part, and whether availability of the part is guaranteed.

Procedures

Operational procedure for preventive maintenance should have a section explaining how to ensure availability of replacement parts. The procedure should require, and define the responsibility for establishing a list with critical replacement parts; and should define the system for managing the replacement parts stock and for ordering parts from distributors and equipment manufacturers.

Records

Records and evidence of compliance consists of parts lists, part inventory records, and information concerning availability of parts from distributors and equipment manufacturers.

Audit

Auditors will ask for documented lists of parts that are maintained in stock or may be required on a very short notice. They will check that the lists are reasonably complete and that all items are either in stock or are available at designated distributors. To test the system, auditors may want to contact some distributors to check availability of specific parts.

Requirement

Establish procedures for packaging and preservation of equipment, tooling and gauging.

This new requirement added in the third edition of the standard asks for documented procedures (or work instructions) for preservation and packaging of equipment, tooling, patterns, fixtures and other types of production aids and gauges. These procedures should define methods to protect equipment in transportation (when it is sent out for repairs or refurbishment, for example) and in storage.

Procedures

For usual types of equipment that are handled routinely, the procedures should be quite specific and require the use of particular cases, boxes, packaging and preservation methods. These procedures would be normally issued on work instruction level. For more unusual cases — for example, transportation or decommissioning of a whole machine — an operational procedure should require that more detailed specifications and instructions be established when needed, and should assign the responsibility for reviewing and issuing such instructions.

Records

There would usually be no written records of packaging and preservation of manufacturing and inspection equipment. The evidence of compliance are the written procedures and instructions, and visual verification of their implementation.

Audit

Auditors will ask for equipment packaging and preservation procedures and work instructions, and will visit the areas where equipment is stored to verify that the procedures are consistently implemented.

Requirement

Document, evaluate and improve equipment maintenance objectives.

This is also a new requirement added in the third edition of QS-9000. It sounds innocent, but it really asks for a whole system of setting objectives for the preventive maintenance program, for evaluating progress toward achieving the objectives, and for improving the objectives. Although this is not explicitly specified in the standard, such system would require development of some measurable indicators of effectiveness (for example, machine downtime, tool wear, process performance, etc.), collection of relevant data, evaluation of the data against defined objectives, and implementation of changes or actions to improve effectiveness.

Procedures

Such system could be defined independently in a dedicated operational procedure, or could be incorporated into other existing systems. For example, the development of suitable measurable indicators and collection of relevant data could be done under the general system for analysis and use of company level data (refer to Section 4.1.5). Setting objectives and evaluation of progress could be done by management reviews (refer to Section 4.1.3) or within the framework of a continuous improvement project (refer to Section 4.5.2). Implementation of changes or actions to improve effectiveness could be also done as a continuous improvement project or, when appropriate, as corrective and preventive action (refer to Section 4.14). To distribute the system in this way, the quality manual should explain how the cycle of defining, evaluating and improving maintenance objectives is incorporated in relevant procedures, and the scope and/or content of these procedures should be extended to include preventive maintenance.

Records

The evidence of compliance are documented objectives, performance data, and records of their evaluation. These can be established in conjunction with management reviews, continuous improvement projects or corrective and preventive actions.

Audit

Auditors will ask for written objectives for the preventive maintenance program and for data demonstrating attainment, or progress toward achieving, the objectives. Over time, auditors will also want to see evidence that effectiveness of preventive maintenance is periodically evaluated by management and that specific improvement actions are being implemented.

4.9.1

Process Monitoring and Operator Instructions

Requirement

Provide process operators with process operating and control instructions.

QS-9000 requires that all process operators must be provided with process operating and process monitoring (SPC) instructions. Process instructions should be prepared using Control Plans, Process Flow Charts, process FMEAs, and other such information developed in the product quality planning phase (see APQP Reference Manual, Section 3.8).

Process operator instructions should include and/or reference such specific information as designated special characteristics, setup instructions, tool change intervals, process control requirements, instructions for use of statistical methods, reaction plans to deal with nonconforming variations, and so forth. For those processes that involve verification of product characteristics, there should be also included such information as inspection and test procedures, sample sizes and sampling frequency, approval and rejection criteria, inspection report forms, nonconformance reaction plans, etc.

Process operator instructions do not need to be established as a single, distinct document. They can be assembled and compiled from a number of different documents, such as drawings, standards, Control Plans, process FMEAs, process sheets, production travelers, equipment operation manuals, and so forth. For more complex processes it is customary to establish a special file (binder) to assemble all the relevant documents instructing in the operation of the process. But there are no specific requirements with regard to format or the level of issuing authority. Process instructions can be issued locally by departmental managers or even supervisors, and they can be established in the form of procedures, instruction sheets, posted notices, samples, photographs, audio- or videotapes, or in any other format.

The whole set of documents constituting process instructions must be available at relevant work stations, and must be controlled in accordance with the requirements of Section 4.5, Document and Data Control.

Procedures

The operational procedure dealing with process instructions should define the functions responsible for establishing, compiling, issuing, and distributing the instructions; should outline their scope; and should explain how to control the instructions (unless the document control procedure already explains it).

Records

Records and evidence of compliance are the process instructions themselves. The evidence that the activities required in the instructions are properly carried out is provided by records of these activities.

Audit

Assessing compliance, auditors will verify that process instructions are available at all relevant workstations, and that the instructions are approved and are controlled. Auditors will also review the scope of the instructions, paying special attention to process setup, monitoring, and verification instructions.

4.9.2   Maintaining Process Control

Requirement

Conduct preliminary process capability studies for all new processes affecting special characteristics.

Although the third edition of QS-9000 suppressed the whole section dealing with preliminary process capability, the corresponding requirements are still included in the PPAP manual.

Preliminary process capability studies must be carried out for all new processes affecting special characteristics. The studies are usually conducted during the production trial run. Results of the studies must be included in the PPAP submission. In many cases explicit customer approval may be required. Process changes should be reported to the customer, and may require re-approval.

Minimum acceptable process capability or performance levels are usually specified by the customers. PPAP manual Section V-D provides default Cpk and Ppk values to be used when customers do not specify other, higher or lower, values. Also in QS-9000 Section II, Customer-specific Requirements, some customers provide their own Cpk and Ppk requirements.

Procedures

Operational procedures dealing with quality planning or PPAP submissions should assign the responsibility for conducting preliminary capability studies; reference specific instructions and acceptance criteria that apply; prescribe general charting and reporting methods; and require implementation of improvement measures, or other corrective action plans, when the required process capability cannot be achieved. There should also be instructions on when and how to submit process capability data for customer review and approval, and to contact and ask customers whether new studies should be conducted in connection with process changes, such as change of product design characteristic, change of material source, new manufacturing location, new tooling, or change in process parameters or equipment.

Specific procedure and techniques for determining process capability are described in the PPAP manual Section V-D, and in Statistical Process Control (SPC) reference manual. These procedures can be adopted and issued as instructions for conducting the studies.

Records

Records and evidence of compliance consist of charts, data sheets, and reports with results of preliminary process capability studies, and the evidence that the results have been reviewed and approved.

Audit

Assessing compliance, auditors will review preliminary process capability reports, noting if the capability studies have been conducted for all relevant processes and process changes, if they have been conducted in accordance with PPAP and other applicable requirements, and if the results have been reviewed and approved internally and/or by the customer. Preliminary process capability reports will be audited in conjunction with the verification of the whole PPAP submission package (refer to Section 4.2.4.1).

Requirement

Monitor and control processes, especially those affecting special characteristics.

The standard encourages suppliers to control all production processes. However, formal process monitoring using SPC charting is only mandatory for those processes that are responsible for special characteristics. Significant process events, such as tool change or machine repair, should be noted on the control charts.

Processes must maintain certain required capability or performance. Acceptance criteria for stable and unstable processes meeting specifications are provided in the PPAP reference manual. Techniques for process control charting and calculation of statistical indices are provided in the SPC reference manual.

The standard emphasizes adherence to Control Plans as a key to monitoring and maintaining process capability or performance. It reminds suppliers that measuring techniques and equipment, sampling plans, acceptance criteria, and reaction plans must be specified in the Control Plans, and be adhered to. There is nothing new in the first three paragraphs of this section. All these requirements are already stated in QS-9000 Section 4.2.3.7 and in the PPAP and the APQP reference manuals.

When processes demonstrate high capability or performance, with Cpk or Ppk values equal or greater than three, the Control Plans can be revised to reduce the sample size or frequency, but this does not exempt from the general requirement to maintain process control.

When a process is unstable or non-capable the supplier should implement measures to identify and segregate nonconforming products (for example, 100% inspection), and initiate corrective actions to assure stability and/or capability of the process. Reliance on product inspection is only acceptable as a temporary measure. The standard explicitly requires that processes be continuously improved.

Procedures

The operational procedure dealing with process control should assign responsibility for establishing the SPC program, and for determining which processes will be controlled and which control techniques used. The procedure should define a system for data collection, charting, statistical analysis, and response actions; and should provide, or refer to, a system for corrective/preventive actions and continuous improvement. The main process control parameters for each relevant process must be documented in the Control Plan.

Job instructions should explain the specific activities and techniques involved in operating the process control system. For example, instructions explaining how to use control charts, how to calculate statistical indices, what to do when process is out of control, etc. The SPC reference manual contains excellent examples of such instructions.

Records

Records and evidence of compliance are the charts and reports established in the course of process monitoring, and documents evidencing implementation of response measures and corrective actions to address process non-conformances.

Audit

Auditors will verify that all processes responsible for special characteristics are controlled and comply with capability and performance requirements. Reviewing control charts, auditors will check that tool changes, machine repairs, excessive variation, and other such special events are identified on the charts, and that appropriate response actions are initiated when required.

4.9.3 Modified Process Control Requirements

This section is a reminder that customers may require other process capability or performance values than those specified in QS-9000 or PPAP, and that the actually required values should be reflected in the Control Plans.

4.9.4   Verification of Job Setups

Requirement

Verify job setups, and provide setup personnel with written instructions.

For the initial run of a job and whenever processing equipment or machines are reset for any reason (for example, maintenance, repair, material changeover, job change, long time elapsed between runs, etc.) and are set up again for production, the setup must be verified before full production is resumed. A method and acceptance criteria for statistical setup verification is provided in the QS-9000 Glossary. The statistical approach is not always required. Simple first-article inspection may be sufficient in some cases, as per customer-specific requirements (refer to Section II or contact the customer).

Procedures

The general system for verification of job setups can be documented either in the procedure dealing with statistical process control or procedure pertaining to in-process inspections. The procedure should instruct when job setup verification is required, who is responsible for carrying it out, what methods should be used, what are the acceptance criteria, and how to establish verification records.

The standard explicitly requires that setup personnel be provided with written job instructions. These instructions would describe in detail the specific methods, equipment and acceptance criteria to be used for verifying setups for specific jobs and processes.

Records

Records and evidence of compliance consist of first-article inspection reports and control charts from statistical verifications. Additional evidence of compliance are current job setup instructions.

Audit

Assessing compliance auditors will verify that process operators have current and approved job setup instructions, and that job setups are verified every time machines or tools are reset. If there are specific customer requirements in this regard, auditors will also verify that the methods used for job setup verification are the same as specified.

4.9.5   Process Changes

This section includes a requirement that process change effective date must be recorded. This is consistent with a similar requirement pertaining to engineering changes (refer to Section 4.5.2.1) and PPAP requirements.

4.9.6   Appearance Items

Requirement

Provide qualified equipment and personnel, and maintain masters for processing and verification of Appearance Items.

QS-9000 and the automotive customers designate certain products as *Appearance Items*. These are products that are visible after completion of a vehicle. Appearance items are subject to special part approval requirements (see PPAP manual), and process control and product verification methods.

For all appearance items there must be approved masters for color, texture, gloss, and other appearance characteristics. The masters are used for verifying process and product conformance. The verification must be carried out by qualified (trained) personnel, and the verification areas must be provided with appropriate lighting and equipment.

Procedures   The operational procedure dealing with process control and inspection activities should acknowledge that approved masters will be used for process control and product verification, and that operators and/or inspectors will be trained, and be provided with appropriate lighting and equipment.

Job instructions may be required to explain in detail how to carry out inspections and tests for appearance characteristics, and how masters should be protected, stored, and used.

Records

Records and evidence of compliance consist of the master approval records, records evidencing that lighting requirements are satisfied, calibration records of evaluation equipment, and personnel training records.

Audit

Assessing compliance, auditors will check that lighting is appropriate and adequate for evaluation of color; that the masters are approved, are properly handled and stored, and are not deteriorated or expired; and that operators and inspectors are trained in evaluation techniques.

* * * * *

Further reading

- Standard ISO 9004 Part 1, Sect. 10 and Sect. 11
- J. Kanholm, *ISO 9000 Quality System*, Chap. 10
- J. Kanholm, *QS-9000 Documentation*, QM Sect. 9, and Operational Procedures OOP-09-01, OOP-09-02, OOP-09-03, OOP-09-04, and OOP-09-05

10 INSPECTION AND TESTING

4.10

Application

Inspection and Testing

Inspection requirements apply to materials, components, and subassemblies intended for incorporation into the final product, products moving through the production processes, and the final products themselves. In some situations physical receiving and in-process inspections are not mandatory. The final inspection, however, must always be carried out.

Documentation

The quality manual should have a section dedicated to inspection and testing. It should contain policies committing the company to inspect and test products in accordance with Control Plans.

There must also be at least three operational procedures explaining how the receiving, in-process, and final inspection systems work, and detailed job instructions explaining how to perform specific inspections and tests.

4.10.1

General

This ISO 9000 subsection does not contain any important or unique requirements. It calls for establishment of inspection procedures, and documentation of the inspection program. The requirement for inspection program (Control Plans) has already been discussed under Section 4.2.3.

4.10.1.1

Acceptance Criteria for Attribute Characteristics

This section communicates the requirement that acceptance criteria for attribute data sampling plans must be zero defects. This applies to incoming, in-process and final products. Control plans, inspection procedures,

work instructions and other documents specifying acceptance criteria should reflect this requirement.

4.10.2   Receiving Inspection and Testing

4.10.2.4   Incoming Product Quality

Requirement

*Inspect or otherwise verify incoming products
and prevent them from being used or processed
before their conformance is verified.*

Verification of received products is mandatory, although
it does not always need to be a physical inspection. When
there is credible evidence that effective controls were
employed by their manufacturer and that the products
have been inspected before dispatch, the receiving inspection can be limited to identification of the products,
review of source inspection records, and verification that
the products and/or their packaging have not been damaged during transportation.

QS-9000 states clearly that received products may be
exempted from physical receiving inspection or testing
when 1) products are supplied with statistical (SPC)
data; or 2) subcontractor has a certified QS-9000 quality system; or 3) product is certified by accredited laboratory. If none of these conditions are satisfied, incoming products must be verified by the supplier before it is
used in production.

The condition regarding subcontractor's quality system
does not explicitly mention QS-9000 as the reference
standard for the system, and does not explicitly require
third-party certification. However, it is understood that
the quality system must at least satisfy all ISO 9000
requirements and those QS-9000 requirements pertaining to quality planning, assurance and control of
processes and products. Thus, in practice, subcontractors
must satisfy nearly all requirements of QS-9000 Section I to qualify for the condition. Regarding certification,
it can be done by either an accredited registrar, the sup-

plier, or the customer. In second-party certification (supplier or customer) the audit program must be maintained continuously with surveillance and follow up audits, as in a third-party certification program.

To prevent uninspected or nonconforming products from being used or processed, the physical arrangement of receiving areas should be laid out to minimize intermingling of products with different inspection status. There should be dedicated locations for products awaiting inspection, and for each stage of the inspection process. Nonconforming products should be quarantined. Products, the conformance of which cannot be determined because they lack certificates or other records, should be considered temporarily nonconforming, and be quarantined. In addition to segregation, products with different inspection status should be appropriately labeled (see Section 4.12).

Procedures

The operational procedure dealing with receiving inspections should provide policy guidelines, and assign the authority for determining how much and what kind of receiving inspection will be applied to a given product, and how this determination is documented and communicated (Control Plans, inspection procedures, etc.). The procedure should also explain the entire system for receiving products, including: checking shipments against purchase orders; reviewing and filing quality records provided; inspecting the received products; establishing inspection records; and labeling the products with their inspection status identification. Job instructions may be required for carrying out specific inspections and tests.

Records

Records and evidence of compliance consist of receiving inspection records and labeling identifying the inspection status of incoming products. Records received from subcontractors, such as statistical data, inspection reports, and certificates of registration of quality systems or laboratory accreditation, are also relevant. Inspection records are discussed in more detail in Section 4.10.5.

Audit

Assessing compliance, auditors will review the receiving inspection records and verify that they are established in accordance with governing procedures. They may pick a sample of closed-out purchase orders and ask for corresponding inspection records, or pick a couple of already received products and start from there. Auditors will also verify that products with different inspection status are adequately segregated and are appropriately labeled. If the opportunity arises, auditors will also want to witness some inspections, verifying that inspectors are qualified, that they use calibrated measuring equipment, and that inspection procedures are available and are used.

4.10.3 In-process Inspection and Testing

Requirement

Carry out in-process inspections to support and validate statistical process control program and other defect prevention measures.

There is a certain ambiguity in the standard with regard to in-process inspections. The original ISO 9000 text provides requirements for in-process inspections, while the QS-9000 add-on paragraph discourages them, promoting defect prevention instead of defect detection. In light of this QS-9000 addition, an in-process inspection should be understood as a measure for monitoring performance of processes rather than acceptance of products. However, a classic in-process inspection is still relevant when processes are unstable or non-capable, and when production runs are too small for application of statistical methods.

All in-process inspections must be specified in the Control Plans. In addition, where production work orders or travelers are used, the inspections can be called out as distinct operations.

In-process inspections can be carried out by production personnel as self-inspections. But the system must be just as formal and in compliance with relevant QS-9000 requirements as if the inspection function was independent. Self-inspections should be documented, carried out, and recorded as distinct operations.

At the points where in-process inspections are prescribed, products should be held and identified to prevent them from moving on to the next processing stage before they are inspected. Suitable holding areas should be provided for this purpose. Products that fail an in-process inspection should be labeled and segregated.

Procedures

The operational procedure dealing with in-process inspections should provide policies and assign authority for deciding at which stages of production in-process inspections will be carried out, and instruct how the inspection program should be documented and communicated. The procedure should also explain who is responsible for carrying out the inspections; how products ought to be identified with respect to their inspections status; how to identify and segregate nonconforming products; and how to establish inspection records. Job instructions may be required for carrying out specific inspections and tests.

Records

Records and evidence of compliance consist of in-process inspection records and implemented measures for holding products until they pass inspection (inspection status identification). Inspection records will be discussed in more detail in Section 4.10.5.

Audit

Assessing compliance, auditors will review in-process inspection records and will verify that adequate measures are employed to prevent uninspected or nonconforming products from being used in the next processing stage. As with all types of inspections, auditors will also examine inspector qualification records, measuring and test equipment, and inspection procedures.

4.10.4

Final Inspection and Testing

Requirement

Inspect finished products to complete the evidence of conformance.

The final inspection is always mandatory. It consists of checking that all required receiving and in-process inspections have been carried out with satisfactory results, and completing the physical inspections and tests that are still needed to fully verify that the product meets specified requirements. Inspectors responsible for the final inspection should review quality records established at preceding stages and check that all operations are completed, that all inspections prescribed by the Control Plans were carried out and, if applicable, that the traceability record is complete. Then, inspectors should carry out the remaining inspections, establish records of these inspections, and release the product. The release is usually recorded by signing or stamping appropriate documents and marking or labeling the released products.

Procedures

The operational procedure dealing with final inspections should explain the two-stage nature of the inspection (i.e., review of preceding inspection records and completion of physical inspections); assign the responsibility for carrying out the inspections; instruct how to identify and segregate conforming and nonconforming products (this could also be a job instruction); and explain what needs to be done to formally release products to stock or shipping.

Job instructions should include checklists for document review (quality records) and the final inspection (i.e., a specification of product characteristics and modes of operation that must be inspected and/or tested). There should also be written inspection and test procedures and acceptance criteria.

Records

Records and evidence of compliance consist of the final inspection records and implemented measures for identifying acceptance and release of products (i.e., tags, labels, sign-offs, etc.). Records will be discussed in more detail in Section 4.10.5.

Audit

Assessing compliance, auditors will review the final inspection records, and will examine the methods used for releasing products. As with other types of inspections, auditors will also examine inspector qualification records, the inspection equipment, and the final inspection and testing procedures. Except for the most simple and obvious cases, the procedures should provide checklists for the review of quality records and for the physical inspections and tests.

4.10.4.1   Layout Inspection and Functional Testing

Requirement

Carry out periodical layout inspections and functional testing.

Layout inspection is a complete verification of all measurements and other characteristics of a product that are specified in design documents. Functional test verifies all specified performance and material requirements.

While ongoing receiving, in-process, and final inspections concentrate on special characteristics, this type of inspection is a comprehensive, periodical verification of all specified product characteristics and performance requirements. The scope, methods, and frequency for layout and functional verification must be specified in the Control Plans, and be approved by the customer.

Procedures

Appropriate operational procedure should define the concept of layout inspection and functional testing; assign the responsibility for determining the scope; methods and frequency for these inspections; and require that comprehensive records be established and made available for customer review.

Job instructions should provide detailed procedures for carrying out the inspections and tests, and for establishing inspection records.

Records

Records and evidence of compliance consist of the layout inspection records and reports (see Section 4.10.5).

Audit

Auditors will verify that methods and frequency used for layout inspections and functional testing are approved by the customer, and that the inspections are carried out regularly and in accordance with applicable procedures.

4.10.4.2   Final Product Audit

Requirement

> *Conduct audits of packaged final product ready for shipment.*

This new section in the third edition of the standard adds a requirement to conduct periodical dock audits. These audits are usually carried out on final product that is ready, and is staged for shipping. The scope of the audit includes comprehensive verification of product characteristics; review of associated statistical data, inspection and testing reports, and other associated quality records; and packaging and labeling of the product and the shipment. Frequency and sample size for this audit should be established based on the criticallity of the product, history of past quality problems and customer complaints, and customer requirements (if any).

Dock audits may be conducted within the framework of internal quality system audits or be carried out by QC inspectors as a supplementary final inspection. The first solution is better with regard to impartiality and independence of the auditor. Using QC inspectors may create a conflict of interest because the audited products have already passed the final inspection and are signed off by QC. However, by inserting this requirement under the section dealing with final inspections, QS-9000 suggests that treating this audit as a supplementary final inspection performed by QC is acceptable.

Procedures

The rules and responsibilities for conducting the final product audit may be documented in procedures dealing with internal quality system audits or procedures dealing with final inspections, depending on how the system is set up. There can also be a separate dedicated procedure for this purpose, which could be relevant if the system is neither merged with internal audits or final inspections. The procedure should assign the responsibility for planning and conducting the audits, explain how to determine frequency and sample size, outline the scope of the audit, and instruct how to report results of the audit. There may also be a need for more detailed job instructions, including checklists.

Records

Records and evidence of compliance consists of an audit plan (frequency, sample size and scope); checklists, reports and other records of the actual inspections, tests and reviews performed; and a final report communicating the overall result of the audit.

Audit

Verifying compliance, auditors will review the final product audit records and reports noting whether the audits are carried out at prescribed frequency and encompass the specified sample, and whether the scope of the audit is complete. Auditors may also ask to witness a dock audit.

4.10.5   Inspection and Test Records

Although this section contains the requirement that inspection records be established and maintained, the requirement is not unique to this section, and is therefore not identified in this book as a distinct requirement. Nearly all QS-9000 activities must be recorded in some way.

In most cases an inspection record does not need to be more elaborate than a sign-off or a stamp on an inspection card or other document associated with the inspected product. For example, the receiving inspection can be recorded by signing off the receiving copy of a purchase order, while the in-process and final inspections can be recorded by signing off the production work order where the inspections are called out. Other commonly used methods for establishing inspection records are: marking up and signing a copy of a drawing, filling out and signing inspection forms, issuing testing reports, and so forth.

Instructions for establishing inspection records should be documented. It can be done on two levels. An operational procedure can provide general requirements, assign responsibilities, and deal with distribution and filing; and specific inspection procedures (job instructions) can provide forms or detailed instructions for recording specific types of inspections. In small companies or when special forms are not used, the whole system can be explained solely in the operational procedures.

4.10.6   Supplier Laboratory Requirements

Requirement   *Establish and document a quality system for in-house laboratories.*

This is a new section in the third edition of QS-9000. It requires establishment of a specific quality system for in-house laboratories and testing facilities, such as chemical, metallurgical, fastener and other labs where samples are tested in controlled conditions and using specialized testing equipment. This section does not apply to product inspection and testing performed outside of a laboratory facility. Laboratories and their quality systems shall be included in the scope of the QS-9000 audit (external and internal).

While QS-9000 requirements for laboratories in this section are obviously modeled after *ISO / IEC Guide 25, General Requirements for the Competence of Calibration and Testing Laboratories,* QS-9000 explicitly states that full compliance with Guide 25 is not required of in-house laboratories. Accreditation to Guide 25 is only required for commercial/independent laboratories and calibration facilities (refer to Sections 4.107 and 4.11.2.b.1).

Requirements of this section can be summarized as follows:

4.10.6.1 - Quality Systems: The laboratory shall document its scope, policies, systems, procedures, instructions and findings.

4.10.6.2 - Personnel: Personnel making professional judgements shall be appropriately qualified with respect to theoretical and practical experience.

4.10.6.3 - Product Identification and Testing: The laboratory shall have procedures and instructions for receipt, identification, handling, protection and retention or disposal of test samples, and shall retain the samples until final data is complete.

4.10.6.4 - Process Control: The laboratory shall establish requirements for environmental conditions (humidity, temperature, dust, sterility, etc.) and shall monitor, control and record the relevant conditions.

4.10.6.5 - Testing and Calibration Methods: The laboratory shall use test and calibration methods specified in international or national standards, and shall verify its capability to perform to the standard specifications before carrying out testing. When standards are not available or are not suitable, the laboratory shall seek customer approval of the proposed methods.

4.10.6.6 - Statistical Methods: When verification results are derived from data (results from large number of tests and/or samples) the data should be evaluated using appropriate statistical techniques.

Procedures

On the documentation level, to comply with these requirements there should be at least one operational procedure explaining the overall quality system in laboratories and a set of work instructions for specific tests, calibrations, use of specialized testing equipment, and monitoring of environmental conditions.

The operational procedure should specify how the scope of the laboratory is to be documented, and generally define the requirements and methods for identifying and handling test samples; monitoring and controlling environmental conditions; selecting and verifying testing methods; selecting and applying statistical techniques; reporting test results; and ensuring that personnel are adequately qualified. This operational procedure would mainly define the policies, responsibilities and authorities for these activities, while referring to specific test procedures and other instructions for detailed description of the actual methods.

The bulk of the required documentation for laboratories will be issued on work instructions level. For every standard test there should be detailed written instructions on how to receive, identify and handle samples; how to check or calibrate testing equipment; how to carry out the test; how to report and process test results; and what to do with the sample after testing. There should also be instructions for checking, calibrating and using test and measuring equipment, and for measuring and controlling relevant environmental conditions.

Records

Records and evidence of compliance consists of written procedures and work instructions; logs, tags, or other means of recording and identifying samples; equipment calibration logs and certificates; test logs, reports and certificates; records of environmental conditions; and records of personnel qualifications and training.

Audit

Certification auditors will focus on the completeness and depth of work instructions and records. They will expect every test, calibration and process in the lab to be documented, and every sample and test result to be consistently recorded. Control and traceability of reference standards, such as standard solutions, material or color standards, will also be audited. Finally, auditors will review personnel training and qualification records, and will verify that testing methods used are compatible with international or national standard specifications or are approved by customers.

4.10.7   Accredited Laboratories

This section simply states that commercial and independent laboratories must be accredited by national accreditation bodies to ISO/IEC Guide 25 or national equivalent. Specific customers may have other requirements (refer to Section II or contact the customer).

* * * * *

Further reading

- Standard ISO 9004 Part 1, Sect. 12
- ISO/IEC Guide 25
- J. Kanholm, *ISO 9000 Quality System*, Chap. 11
- J. Kanholm, *QS-9000 Procedures*, QM Sect. 10, and Operational Procedures QOP-10-01, QOP-10-02, QOP-10-03, and QOP-10-04

11 CONTROL OF INSPECTION, MEASURING, AND TEST EQUIPMENT

4.11 Control of Inspection, Measuring, and Test Equipment

4.11.1 General

Application

Requirements in this section apply to measuring and test equipment used to verify conformance of products and to qualify and maintain production tools. Strictly speaking, measuring equipment used in production does not have to be included unless it is used for controlling processes (process control is in fact a form of in-process inspection). Unless there are particular reasons to the contrary, all measuring and test equipment should be controlled, regardless of whether it is used in inspection or production. In modern quality assurance systems, where production personnel are involved in inspections and products are verified indirectly through process control, there is no clear distinction between inspection and production functions and areas.

In addition to conventional measuring instruments, the requirements apply also to test software (computer), and comparative test hardware such as jigs, templates, patterns, etc.

Documentation

The quality manual should have a section dedicated to management and control of measuring equipment. It should contain policies committing the company to evaluate, calibrate, and control the measuring equipment; a short outline procedure explaining how these policies are implemented; and references to operational procedures and work instructions that apply.

There must also be an operational procedure explaining the measuring equipment control system, and specific calibration procedures (job instructions) explaining how to calibrate various kinds of measuring and test equipment.

4.11.2   Control Procedure

Requirement

Calibrate and/or check measuring and test equipment, and maintain calibration records.

Standards used for calibration and checking of measuring equipment must be certified and be traceable to an internationally or nationally recognized standard.

Every calibration should be evidenced by a calibration record. The record should identify the calibrated instrument by its name, type, and serial number; identify the standard used for calibration and provide its traceability number to the national standard; list the calibrated functions of the instrument and the calibration results; identify the temperature, pressure, or other relevant environmental conditions; indicate the next calibration due date; identify the calibration procedure (work instruction); and identify the person performing the calibration. These records are often called calibration certificates. QS-9000 also requires that when gauges are received for calibration, their condition and actual readings must be recorded before they are calibrated.

Calibrated equipment should be marked with calibration stickers indicating the last and the next calibration date. Measuring and test equipment that is exempt from calibration must be clearly identified with warning labels, and should not be available in inspection areas.

Procedures

The operational procedure dealing with calibration should define which types of equipment must be calibrated; what restrictions govern the of use of uncalibrated equipment; who is responsible for the calibrating; the general policy regarding traceability of calibration standards; and the requirements for establishing and maintaining calibration records.

On the work instruction level, the calibration procedures should instruct how to calibrate and/or check specific types of equipment; specify which calibration standards should be used; and provide forms or detailed instructions for establishing calibration certificates. Calibration procedures may not be necessary when calibration instructions are provided in equipment manuals. When equipment is sent out for calibration there is, of course, no need for calibration procedures.

Records

Records and evidence of compliance consist of the calibration procedures, calibration certificates, and the stickers identifying equipment calibration status.

Audit

Assessing compliance, auditors will check the calibration status of equipment found in production and inspection areas, and will ask for the corresponding calibration certificates. Auditors will also review a sample of calibration procedures and may ask for checking and recalibration of some instruments to verify that they were indeed accurately calibrated, and that personnel performing calibrations know how to apply calibration procedures. Reviewing calibration records, auditors will verify that traceability of masters used for calibration is documented, and that gauge condition and actual readings have been recorded prior to calibration.

Requirement

Identify, maintain, and safeguard measuring and test equipment.

The backbone of any measuring and test equipment management system is an inventory and status list. Every piece of equipment on the list is identified by its type and serial number, its usual location, the prescribed calibration periodicity, the last calibration date, and the next due date for calibration. The list is usually maintained on a computer. A standard database or a special software for management of calibration equipment can be used for this purpose.

Measuring and test equipment must be adequately maintained, protected, and stored. Equipment should be stored in dedicated cabinets or drawers, and protective boxes should be used when provided. Defective or otherwise unsuitable equipment should be segregated and/or identified with warning labels.

The measuring equipment also must be safeguarded against unauthorized adjustments that would invalidate the calibration setting. The most effective measure is to seal the adjustment screws, or otherwise physically protect against tampering. If this is not possible or practical, there at least should be a clearly stated and communicated policy that unauthorized adjustments are prohibited. It can be displayed on warning labels or written in an appropriate procedure.

Procedures

The operational procedure dealing with management of measuring equipment should explain how to establish and maintain the equipment inventory and status list; who is responsible for updating the list; what to do when a piece of equipment cannot be located; and how to identify, maintain, store, and safeguard the equipment.

Records

Records and evidence of compliance consist of the equipment inventory and status list, calibration stickers, and the evidence that equipment is properly maintained and stored.

Audit

Assessing compliance, auditors will check the actual status of measuring equipment found in different areas against the equipment status list. They may also start from the other end: pick a couple of gauges from the list and check that the gauges can indeed be found in the designated areas and locations, and that they are correctly identified with regard to their calibration status. Auditors will also verify that equipment is properly identified, maintained, and stored, and that it is safeguarded against unauthorized adjustments.

Requirement

Reassess validity of previously made measurements when measuring equipment is found to be out of calibration.

When an out-of-calibration or otherwise unacceptable instrument is found in inspection or production areas, all measurements for which this instrument was used should be reassessed. In practice it means that the affected products should be recalled to the inspection area and be verified again using approved and calibrated gauges. If the products have been already shipped, the customer must be notified.

The event of finding an unacceptable gauge should be documented and brought to the attention of the responsible functions. When appropriate, corrective actions should be proposed and implemented.

Procedures

The operational procedure dealing with measuring and test equipment should explain how to investigate suspect measurements and how to document these events, and should require that customers be notified when suspect products have been shipped. Investigation of causes and implementation of corrective actions should also be addressed in the procedure (may be by reference to other procedures).

Records

Records and evidence of compliance consist of nonconforming product reports, corrective action reports, internal audit reports, customer notifications, and other such documents established in the course of identifying and investigating the use of unacceptable measuring equipment.

Audit

Auditors will ask whether there were instances of finding out-of-calibration gauges and will review documents and records pertaining to such events. Auditors will also review records of gauge condition and accuracy at the time when gauges were returned for calibration (precalibration condition records must be kept per Section 4.11.3). If a precalibration record shows that a gauge was out of specified error limit, auditors will expect that the use of the gauge would have been investigated. Auditors will also check a sample of active gauges to verify that all are calibrated and approved for current use.

4.11.2.b.1   Calibration Services

Requirement

> *Establish and document a quality system for in-house calibration laboratories, and use only accredited commercial calibration facilities.*

In this new section added in the third edition, QS-9000 requires that all in-house calibration labs must comply with requirements of Section 4.10.6, Supplier Laboratory Requirements. In practice, this means that a company that performs any in-house calibrations is presumed to operate a laboratory and this laboratory must comply with Section 4.10.6. This may be too severe for a company that calibrates only a limited number of simple instruments and does not have an identifiable calibration lab. But the standard does not seem to allow for any exceptions. Requirements of Section 10.4.6 are explained in the preceding chapter.

This new section also requires that outside commercial calibration services must be accredited to ISO/IEC Guide 25, or be assessed by an OEM customer to meet the intent of the guide. As an alternative, calibration may be performed by the original equipment manufacturer.

Procedures

Documentation requirements for in-house laboratories are discussed in the preceding chapter. They are quite extensive, especially with regard to detailed work instructions explaining how to calibrate specific types of equipment, ensure traceability, and establish calibration records.

For outside commercial calibration services, the quality manual should state that only accredited facilities may be used, and appropriate operational procedure should explain how to qualify these facilities. This can be included in the procedure dealing with evaluation of subcontractors. Acceptable calibration services should be included in the approved subcontractor list.

Records

Records and evidence of compliance consists of calibration lab procedures, work instructions and records; and appropriate accreditations and certifications for outside calibration facilities.

Audit

Comments regarding the audit of in-house calibration laboratories are the same as for Section 10.4.6 (refer to the preceding chapter). With regard to outside calibration services, auditors will ask for the evidence that these facilities are appropriately accredited or certified to comply with, or meet the intent of, ISO/IEC Guide 25.

4.11.3   Inspection, Measuring, and Test Equipment Records

Records are discussed in connection with each requirement individually. A new and important requirement in this subsection is that precalibration condition and actual readings of gauges must be recorded.

4.11.4   Measuring System Analysis

Requirement

Evaluate all measurement systems referenced in Control Plans.

All measurement systems used for verification of special characteristics, i.e., those specified in the Control Plans, must be evaluated and be determined acceptable for the intended use. The evaluation must be submitted for part approval (refer to PPAP manual). Techniques, procedures, and acceptance criteria for analyzing and qualifying measurement systems are provided in the Measurement System Analysis (MSA) reference manual. The MSA manual contains specific instructions, charts, and examples that may be directly adopted as third-level instructions for carrying out measurement system studies. QS-9000 explicitly requires that the manual be used for determining acceptability of measurement systems.

For most systems, it is the spread in variation, including repeatability, reproducibility (Gauge R&R), and stability, that is the main characteristic to be evaluated. Bias and linearity (accuracy and its variation through the gauge range) may also be important for some systems. The acceptability criteria are usually expressed in terms of gauge system error as a percentage of specified part tolerance. Systems with over 30 percent error are not acceptable. The MSA manual also requires that gauge graduation must be at least one-tenth of the tolerance.

Procedures

Measurement system analysis and qualification is usually dealt with in the general procedure for measuring and test equipment. The procedure should identify the function responsible for studying measurement systems; provide or reference instructions for analyzing the systems (MSA manual); provide or reference acceptance criteria; and instruct how to prepare reports and formally approve specific systems for use in verification of specific products (Control Plans, for example).

Specific procedures, charts, and forms to be used for evaluating measurement systems may be issued as third-level job instructions. Relevant procedures included in the MSA manual may be directly adopted as job instructions (contact publishers for copyright permission before copying portions of the manual).

Records

Records and evidence of compliance are measurement system evaluation reports and formal approvals of specific systems for use in verification of specific products.

Audit

Auditors will check the Control Plans to verify that specific systems are prescribed for verification of processes and products; will review the measurement system evaluation reports; and will verify that systems satisfy the specified acceptance criteria. In the field, auditors will check that in fact only the specified and qualified measurement systems are used, and that individual pieces of equipment are identifiable to the evaluation reports evidencing their suitability.

* * * * *

Further reading

- Standard ISO 9004 Part 1, Sect. 13
- ISO/IEC Guide 25 and ISO 10012-1
- J. Kanholm, *ISO 9000 Quality System*, Chap. 11
- J. Kanholm, *QS-9000 Documentation*, QM Sect. 11, and Op. Prc. QOP-11-01, QOP-11-02 and QOP-10-04

12 INSPECTION AND TEST STATUS

4.12

Application

Inspection and Test Status

Inspection and test status identification requirements apply to materials, components, and subassemblies intended for incorporation into the final product, and to the final products themselves. The identification should be maintained from receipt and during all stages of production, assembly, storage, and delivery.

Documentation

The quality manual should have a section dedicated to inspection and test status. It should contain policies committing the company to identify inspection status of products and maintain the identification; a short outline procedure explaining how the policies are implemented; and references to the operational procedures that apply.

On the operational procedure level, the inspection status identification system can be explained in a dedicated procedure, or in procedures dealing with inspections. Inspection status identification can be considered to be the last step of an inspection operation.

Requirement

Identify inspection and test status of products, to ensure that only products that have passed required inspections are used or shipped.

The result of every inspection should be evidenced by appropriate identification of the inspected products. It is not sufficient to identify only failed products. Passed products must also be positively identified. The identification means can include: marking, labeling, or tagging products and/or the containers or packaging holding them; inspection records, such as sign-offs in production work orders or other documents that travel with the products; and physical segregation of products with different inspection status. Physical location of products in normal production flow is not sufficient to identify their inspection status, unless the production flow transfer is automated. Physical location is also acceptable when specific dedicated areas are used and these areas are identified by posted signs. Whenever possible and practical, nonconforming products should be segregated in addition to labeling or marking.

Procedures

The operational procedure for identifying inspection status of products should explain which identification measures are used for different kinds of products and various production stages; and who is responsible for maintaining the inspection status identification system. The procedure should also instruct all personnel to safeguard and maintain the inspection status identification.

Records

No records are required. The evidence of implementation are the labels, tags, or other means of identification that are applied to products to indicate their inspection status.

Audit

Assessing compliance, auditors will verify that all products at all stages are properly identified as to their inspection status. A common problem is loss of the receiving inspection status identification when materials or components are transferred from material storage to production areas.

* * * * *

Further reading

- Standard ISO 9004 Part 1, Sect. 11.7

- J. Kanholm, *ISO 9000 Quality System*, Chap. 10 and Chap. 11

- J. Kanholm, *QS-9000 Procedures*, QM Sect. 12, and Operational Procedure QOP-12-01

13 CONTROL OF NONCONFORMING PRODUCT

4.13

Application

Control of Nonconforming Product

Requirements of this section apply to nonconforming and suspect materials, components, and subassemblies intended for incorporation into the final product, and to the final products themselves. Suspect products are products and materials with unknown or uncertain inspection status. For example, it can be a batch of components where one nonconforming component was identified in a sample, or a shipment of components that was received without the required material testing certificates. All types of nonconformances, regardless of how insignificant they seem, should be processed through the nonconforming product control system.

Documentation

The quality manual should have a section dedicated to the control of nonconforming products. It should contain a policy committing the company to identify, document, review, and disposition nonconforming products and, when applicable, reinspect repairs and rework. There should be a short outline procedure explaining how the policy is implemented, and references to the operational procedures that apply.

There must also be an operational procedure explaining the nonconforming product control system.

4.13.1

Requirement

General

Identify, segregate, and document nonconforming and suspect products.

Product is considered nonconforming when it is in any way different from the specified product and/or approved sample. Nonconformance can be a characteristic that is out of tolerance; a workmanship problem; differing color, texture, or surface finish; an appearance defect; damage resulting from improper handling or storage; and so forth.

Product nonconformances are usually detected at various inspection and testing points. They may also be found by customers, and the products be returned for repair or replacement. As soon as a nonconformance is detected, the nonconforming product should be identified — with a red HOLD, NONCONFORMANCE, or REJECTED label, for example — and be segregated, or even quarantined, whenever possible.

The nature of the nonconformance must be documented (recorded). This is usually done in a nonconformance report form. The same form can also be used to record the disposition and, when relevant, reinspection of repaired or reworked products. The form can have the following four sections:

Heading — for identifying the product(s) and the location where they were found.

Description of Nonconformance — for documenting the nature of the nonconformance.

Disposition — for recording the decision regarding what should be done with the nonconforming product.

Close-out — for recording acceptance of the product after rework or repair.

Such a form is provided and explained in the *QS-9000 Documentation* software.

Copies of nonconformance reports should be distributed to functions concerned; for example, sales, purchasing, production control, and quality assurance.

Procedures   The operational procedure dealing with control of nonconforming products (or relevant inspection procedures) should explain how nonconforming products are identified and segregated; how nonconformances are recorded; and how nonconformances are reported to other functions concerned, including those responsible for making disposition decisions.

Records

Records and evidence of compliance are nonconformance reports documenting product nonconformances. The use of labels, tags, and other means to identify nonconforming products, and their segregation, provide additional evidence of implementation.

Audit

Assessing compliance, auditors will verify that all nonconforming products, wherever they are found, are clearly identified and are segregated. Auditors will also review nonconformance reports, noting if the reports are being established consistently every time a nonconformance is identified, and if they are further processed and distributed to document the disposition decisions and inform other functions concerned.

4.13.1.1 Suspect Material or Product

This section states that Element 4.13 of the standard applies also to suspect material or product, i.e., where the inspection and test status is uncertain.

4.13.1.2 Visual Identification

This section reinforces the requirement that any nonconforming or suspect product must be identified by a tag, label, physical location in a designated area (quarantine) or by other means that visually identify the product as nonconforming.

4.13.2 Review and Disposition of Nonconforming Product

Requirement

Review nonconforming products and decide whether they should be accepted, reworked, repaired, regraded, or scrapped.

There are five possibilities for the disposition of nonconforming products.

- **Accept-as-is**: when the nonconformance is minor and does not affect functional aspects of the product.
- **Rework**: when nonconforming product can be reprocessed or reworked to fully meet specified requirements.
- **Repair**: when the nonconformance can be repaired to meet at least the most critical requirements, but full conformance cannot be restored.
- **Regrade**: when nonconforming product can be accepted to less stringent requirements and is suitable for use for alternative applications.
- **Scrap**: when the nonconforming product cannot be used, reworked, or repaired.

Accept-as-is and repair options leave some degree of nonconformance in a product and do, therefore, require concession from the customer (see the last requirement in this section).

The authority for the disposition of nonconforming product must be defined in a procedure. The authority can be assigned on different levels depending on the nature of the nonconformance and the product, and the disposition decision itself. For example, decisions to rework or scrap can usually be made by supervisors or even production personnel, while accept-as-is and repair decisions may require involvement of higher authority.

The disposition decision must be documented and authorized with a signature. It is best to do it in the same nonconformance report that is opened when a nonconforming product is first identified. With accept-as-is, regrade, and scrap decisions the nonconformance report can be closed out right away. When the decision is to rework or repair, closing out the report must wait until the products are reinspected.

Procedures   The operational procedure dealing with the disposition of nonconforming products should define the possible disposition decisions, and provide guidelines and assign the authority for making the decisions. The procedure should also explain how to use the nonconformance reports for recording nonconforming product dispositions.

Records

Records and the evidence of compliance are the nonconformance reports that document the disposition decisions, and the records evidencing that repaired and reworked products are reinspected.

Audit

Assessing compliance, auditors will review the nonconformance reports, noting if dispositions are being authorized at the appropriate level. They will also verify that accepted nonconformances are recorded to denote the actual condition, and that repaired and reworked products are reinspected.

4.13.2.1   Prioritized Reduction Plans

Requirement

Establish and implement a nonconformance reduction plan, and track progress toward achieving the reduction goals.

Although included in this section dealing with nonconforming product, this requirement pertains to continuous improvement. Section 4.2.5, Continuous Improvement, already includes nonconformance (scrap, rework, and repair) reduction in a list of recommended improvement projects. With this requirement, the nonconformance reduction project is elevated from recommended to mandatory status on the continuous improvement list.

To comply, quantities and ratios of different types of nonconformances should be recorded and reported periodically. This is usually done using graphs and charts showing quantities, ratios, and trends over time. There should also be a plan to reduce the quantities and/or ratios of improved target goals, and a system for tracking progress towards the planned goals. It is not required to continuously improve performance for all types of nonconformances at once. The reduction plan and effort can prioritize the improvement projects having highest impact on overall quality.

Procedures

The system for tracking and reduction of nonconformances can be either documented in the nonconforming product procedure, or in the procedures dealing with continuous improvement. The procedure should assign the responsibilities and define systems for categorizing nonconformances; compiling statistics; reviewing data and trends; setting improvement priorities and targets; and implementing improvement projects to achieve reductions.

Records

Records and evidence of compliance are nonconformance statistics and trend reports, and plans to reduce nonconformances. Supplementary evidence is provided by records of related improvement projects.

Audit

Auditors will verify that nonconformance statistics and trends are regularly compiled and analyzed, and that the trends generally show improvement. All types of nonconformances should be tracked and analyzed. Auditors will also ask which types of nonconformances are currently targeted for reduction, what are the reduction target goals, and what is being done to achieve the goals.

4.13.3   Control of Reworked Product

Requirement

Provide work instructions for rework operations.

This section requires that personnel conducting rework operations must be provided with written instructions. The reason for the requirement is that since rework operations cannot be planned in advance and rework processes are not formally qualified and approved, the rework operator instructions is the only way to document these processes. When rework is basically a repetition of one or more production processes, the rework instructions may simply list those processes and refer to appropriate process operator instructions. Rework instructions must be reviewed, approved, and authorized for use as other process operator instructions.

Procedures

The system for establishment and use of rework instructions can be documented in the procedure dealing with control of nonconforming product, or the procedure for establishing process operator instructions. The procedure (or the quality manual) should contain a policy requiring that all rework operations, including the most simple and obvious, must be documented in written instructions. The procedure should provide guidelines and assign the responsibility for establishing the instructions.

Records

The record and evidence of compliance consists of nonconformance reports and rework instructions. Reworked product inspection records are also relevant.

Audit

Assessing compliance, auditors will verify that rework instructions are established and are used for all rework operations. Reviewing files with nonconformance reports, auditors will look for reports with rework dispositions and will ask for copies of corresponding rework instructions. Auditors will also verify that rework instructions are authorized and are available in relevant work areas.

4.13.4 Engineering Approved Product Authorization

Requirement

Seek customer authorization for shipping product that is in any way different from currently approved.

This requirement obliges suppliers to follow the Engineering Approved Product Authorization (EAPA) process for seeking and obtaining customer concession to accept nonconforming products. The EAPA authorization is usually granted for a limited time and/or quantity. Suppliers are obliged to keep a record of the expiration date or authorized quantity, and to ensure that full compliance of products can be achieved before the authorization expires. The process also requires that suppliers concur with EAPA requests from their subcontractors before they are forwarded to the customer. Products shipped on authorization must be properly identified.

Procedures

There is no need for a step-by-step procedure for requesting EAPAs. It is sufficient to state a policy commitment that EAPA authorizations will be requested for shipment of nonconforming products; that subcontractor requests will be reviewed before they are forwarded to the customer; that conforming products will be shipped after expiration of an EAPA; and that products shipped on authorization will be properly identified. These commitments can be stated in the quality manual and/or the procedure dealing with control of nonconforming product.

Records

Records and evidence of compliance are the EAPAs and, when an EAPA request is submitted by a subcontractor, records demonstrating that the request has been reviewed and approved by the supplier.

Audit

Assessing compliance, auditors will review the EAPAs against shipping records to verify that product on authorization is not shipped after the EAPA is expired. Auditors will also verify that EAPA shipments are properly identified.

* * * * *

Further reading

- Standard ISO 9004 Part 1, Sect. 14
- J. Kanholm, *ISO 9000 Quality System*, Chap. 11
- J. Kanholm, *QS-9000 Documentation*, QM Sect. 13, and Operational Procedure QOP-13-01

14 CORRECTIVE AND PREVENTIVE ACTION

4.14 Corrective and Preventive Action

4.14.1 General

Application

Corrective and preventive actions must be taken in response to identified and potential nonconformances in products, production equipment, processes, measuring and testing equipment, and the quality system itself. All activities that can potentially identify a nonconformance — such as inspections, process control, customer service, purchasing, and internal auditing — should interface with and use the system for implementing corrective and preventive actions.

Documentation

The quality manual should have a section dedicated to implementing corrective and preventive actions. It should contain policies committing the company to review nonconformances, investigate their causes, and implement corrective and preventive actions, as appropriate. The manual should also contain a short outline procedure explaining how the policies are implemented, and reference the operational procedures that apply.

The number of procedures required to document the corrective and preventive action process depends on how many different systems for various types of actions are used. Some, especially larger, companies may want to have different systems for corrective actions to address subcontractor quality problems, noncompliances detected by internal audits, nonconforming products returned by customers, and so forth. Smaller companies can have just one system for processing all types of corrective actions. In addition to corrective and preventive action procedures there should be an independent procedure for handling and processing of customer complaints.

4.14.1.1   Problem Solving Methods

Requirement

Use disciplined problem-solving methods.

Disciplined problem-solving methods means that problems are documented, solutions are planned, the responsibilities for implementation of solutions are assigned, the effectiveness of implemented solutions is verified, and the results of the whole process are recorded. In some cases, especially when product nonconformances are identified by customers and products are returned, customers require that a special procedure for analyzing nonconformances and reporting findings is followed (refer to requirement for analyzing and testing returned products).

Procedures

There is no need for a special procedure explaining problem-solving methods. Compliance with this requirement will be sufficiently documented when each procedure dealing with corrective and preventive actions prescribes a system that includes the elements of problem-solving methods listed in the preceding paragraph.

Records

Records and evidence of compliance are corrective action requests and various reports established in the course of implementing solutions and verifying their effectiveness.

Audit

Assessing compliance, auditors will verify that all solutions to quality problems are processed through the formal system for requesting and implementing corrective actions. Evidence that there are spontaneous and undocumented problem-solving projects may lead to a non-compliance with this requirement.

4.14.1.2   Mistake Proofing

This new section added to the third edition of the standard requires that mistake proofing techniques be used in corrective and preventive actions, when appropriate. Similar requirement to use mistake proofing techniques in quality planning in discussed in this book in Section 4.2.3.6. The same issues apply to this section.

4.14.2

Corrective Action

Requirement

Establish a system for effective handling of customer complaints.

The function responsible for handling customer complaints should be clearly defined. In larger companies it is usually the customer service department. In small companies, or when the nature of products is such that a special customer service function is not necessary, customer complaints can be handled by sales, marketing, or quality assurance. The function charged with the responsibility for handling customer complaints must be clearly indicated in the organizational charts and/or specifications of departmental responsibilities.

All customer complaints should be logged and entered into the customer complaint processing system. Complaints under processing should be labeled, stamped, or provided with a cover sheet indicating their current processing status. There should be a clear policy for responding to customers and for making decisions regarding refunds, replacements, and repairs. When customers return nonconforming products, the products should be labeled, segregated, evaluated, and dispositioned in compliance with the requirements that generally apply to the control of nonconforming products (see preceding section). The complaints should be communicated to other functions concerned, such as marketing, engineering, production, quality control, etc.

All actions and communication related to a customer complaint should be recorded. The process and authorizations for closing out a complaint should be defined, and the retention period for closed-out complaints should be specified (see Section 4.16, Quality Records).

Investigation of the problems that may have caused customer complaint and/or product nonconformance, and the implementation of corrective actions, will be discussed in connection with the next requirement.

Procedures

There should be a separate procedure for handling customer complaints. The procedure should define which function is responsible for receiving and processing the complaints; provide policies for responding to customers and making decisions regarding refunds and replacements of defective products; provide channels for communication with other functions concerned, especially those responsible for investigating causes of nonconformances and implementing corrective actions; and instruct how to close out and file the complaints.

Records

Records and evidence of compliance consist of the letters, memos, and reports evidencing communication with the complaining customer and with other functions concerned; and records of the actions taken to redress the customer and correct the underlying problems.

Audit

Assessing compliance, auditors will review the customer complaint files to verify that the complaining customers receive a response, that the underlying problems are communicated to other functions concerned, and that corrective actions are taken when appropriate. Auditors will also note how long it takes to process complaints, and whether there is a system for tracking the status of opened complaints.

Requirement

Investigate causes of product, process, and quality system nonconformances and implement corrective actions.

The system for investigating quality problems and implementing corrective actions should include the following elements: an identification and description of the nonconforming condition; a decision if a request for corrective action is the appropriate response; a formal request for corrective action; a plan for corrective action and a deadline for its implementation; and a verification that the corrective action has been implemented and that it is effective.

The authority for deciding whether a corrective action will be requested is usually placed relatively high in the organization, especially when implementation of the action is likely to cause disruption and require considerable resources.

Corrective action requests should be addressed directly to the department or function that is responsible for the nonconforming condition and is capable of correcting it. The responsible party should acknowledge that the description of the nonconforming condition is accurate, and should propose, in writing, the action to be taken and the estimated date of completion. The requesting party should then review and approve the proposed action and, on or immediately after the agreed completion date, should follow up to verify that the action has been implemented and that it is effective. The whole process can be documented using a corrective action request form containing separate blocks for description of the nonconforming condition, proposal of the corrective action to be taken, and follow-up verification. (Such a form is provided in the *QS-9000 Documentation* software.)

As mentioned at the top of this section, the need for implementation of a corrective action can be identified by different functions and/or departments within the company. Typically, these are quality control, customer service, process control, purchasing, and internal quality auditing. One possibility is to allow each such function to have its own independent system for requesting and implementing corrective actions, and the other is to have a central system through which all requests for corrective actions must be processed, regardless of where and how they originate.

Procedures

The operational procedure dealing with corrective actions should clearly define the function(s) vested with the authority to request corrective actions; explain the process; and instruct how to use the corrective action request forms. When different functions and/or departments operate their own systems, each should have a separate procedure.

Records

Records and evidence of compliance are the corrective action requests. Open requests under processing should be appropriately organized and/or logged to ensure that they will be followed up when due. Closed out requests should be filed and retained for a specified period of time.

Audit

Assessing compliance, auditors will review the corrective action requests, noting whether the requests are processed in a timely manner and are properly closed out; i.e., are signed off for the verification of their implementation and effectiveness.

4.14.2.1   Returned Product Test/Analysis

Requirement

Test and analyze nonconforming products returned by customers.

This automotive requirement reinforces the general requirement that nonconforming products be tested and analyzed to determine the root causes of nonconformances. For nonconforming products returned by customers, the suppliers are obliged to establish and maintain records of these analysis and, when requested, make them available for customer review.

Procedures

In larger companies it may be appropriate to establish a special procedure for processing nonconforming products returned by customers. Otherwise, the process can be documented in the procedure dealing with customer complaints. The procedure should define the system for documenting nonconformances, testing and analyzing the product to determine causes, and reporting the findings. The procedure should also assign the responsibility and authority for determining whether a corrective action is required.

Records

Records and evidence of compliance are reports with results of testing and analysis of nonconforming products returned by customers. There should also be evidence that corrective actions are implemented when appropriate.

Audit

Assessing compliance, auditors will ask for a log or a listing of customer returns and will investigate specific cases to verify whether returned products are being consistently tested and analyzed. No matter how simple and obvious the nonconformance, auditors will expect to find a report for every case of returned products. Auditors will also ask what actions have been taken to prevent recurrence of nonconformances.

4.14.2.2 Corrective Action Impact

This section reminds that a corrective action applied to one problem can often be used to address another, similar problem. To comply with this section, the procedure dealing with corrective actions should encourage, if not require, that corrective actions be evaluated for application to other similar processes or products.

4.14.3 Preventive Action

Requirement

Review process and quality records to identify potential causes of nonconformances, and implement preventive actions.

The distinction between corrective and preventive action is that corrective action deals with actual nonconformances and preventive action deals with potential nonconformances. The only difference in processing of corrective and preventive action is the first step of identifying the problem that requires attention. All other steps of the process can be exactly the same for both, and there is usually no need to have independent systems and procedures.

The usual sources of information needed to identify potential quality problems are process performance data, product nonconformance reports, equipment maintenance records, and other quality records. Most of the recorded problems are usually minor and, when looked at individually, may not warrant initiation of corrective actions. But when analyzed over time, the records may show some unfavorable trends that must be dealt with to reduce their frequency and/or prevent occurrence of more serious problems.

Analysis of quality performance data is also required in several other sections of the standard; for example, Section 4.1.5 Analysis and Use of Company-Level Data, or Section 4.2.5 Continuous Improvement. With respect to prevention of product nonconformances, this requirement has already been stated in Section 4.13.3, wherein suppliers are obliged to reduce nonconformance rates.

Procedures

There is usually no need for a separate procedure dealing exclusively with preventive actions. The corrective and preventive action systems can be documented together, or preventive actions can be included in the procedure dealing with continuous improvement. The procedure should assign the responsibility for the analysis of quality records; specify which records should be analyzed; and explain how the results of the analysis should be reported and used for initiating preventive actions.

Records

Records and evidence of compliance are reports and records from reviews of historical quality performance data, and the preventive action requests.

Audit

Assessing compliance, auditors will review the preventive action requests, and will ask for the evidence that quality records and process performance data are being regularly reviewed and analyzed to determine where preventive actions may be required.

* * * * *

Further reading

- Standard ISO 9004 Part 1, Sect. 15

- J. Kanholm, *ISO 9000 Quality System*, Chap. 16

- J. Kanholm, *QS-9000 Documentation*, QM Sect. 14, and Operational Procedures QOP-14-01 and MOP-14-02

15 HANDLING, STORAGE, PACKAGING, PRESERVATION AND DELIVERY

4.15 Handling, Storage, Packaging, Preservation, and Delivery

The product handling and preservation requirements apply to all products, including materials, components, and subassemblies.

Application

The storage requirements apply to all locations where products are held awaiting use or delivery. They include staging locations in receiving areas, storage locations for purchased materials and components, the locations in production areas where products are temporarily held awaiting inspection and/or the next processing stage, storage locations for manufactured parts and sub-assemblies, and finished product stocks.

The packaging requirements apply to both the product and shipping packaging.

The delivery requirements apply to all shipments of finished products.

Documentation

The quality manual should have a section dedicated to handling, storage, packaging, preservation, and delivery. It should contain policies committing the company to comply with all requirements discussed in this section. The manual should also contain a short outline procedure explaining how the policies are implemented for each activity, and reference the operational procedures that apply.

There must also be an operational procedure for each activity. Handling and preservation are often documented in one procedure. Work instructions are required when special handling and/or preservation techniques are used.

4.15.1   **General**

4.15.2   **Handling**

Requirement

Use product handling methods and equipment that prevent damage and deterioration.

In most companies, product handling is quite routine. Products are held in various types of containers, tanks, and on pallets, and are transported around production and storage areas using carts, forklift trucks, and cranes. If handling operations are as basic as these, the only issues are selection of appropriate handling equipment; maintenance of the equipment; and, for cranes and fork-lift trucks, training of equipment operators.

When special handling techniques are necessary — such as use of gloves, electrostatic mats, double bagging, etc. — the techniques should be explained in detailed work instructions, and/or personnel should be trained in their use.

Procedures

Whether special techniques are used or not, there should be an operational procedure dealing with product handling. It can be combined with the procedure addressing preservation of products (see requirements under Section 4.15.5). The procedure should assign the responsibility for selecting and maintaining suitable containers, transportation equipment, and other product handling equipment; specify the requirements for qualifications and training of equipment operators; and, when applicable, reference work instructions for particular handling techniques.

Records

Product handling does not usually require establishment of any records. However, documents such as equipment certificates (especially cranes) and equipment operator training records are relevant for evidencing compliance.

Audit

Assessing compliance, auditors will observe and note if product handling equipment is appropriate and is well maintained; if personnel follow work instructions when using special handling techniques; and if there are any signs of products being damaged, or being at risk, because of inappropriate handling. When relevant, auditors will also review equipment certificates and operator training records.

4.15.3 Storage

Requirement

Provide designated storage areas.

The kinds of storage areas to which this requirement applies are listed at the beginning of this section. In this requirement, *designated storage area* means an area, clearly contained and segregated from other adjacent areas, that is exclusively dedicated and authorized for storage of particular kinds of products. Storage areas do not always need to be separate rooms or be enclosed by a fence. A dedicated rack of shelves or a yellow line on the floor will, in most cases, provide sufficient segregation. When different kinds of products are stored in the same general storage area, each kind should have its designated location within the area.

Designation and authorization of a storage area should be identified by posted signs and be documented in a layout plan or a procedure.

Procedures

The operational procedure dealing with storage should include, or reference, a plan or a list designating specific locations for storing particular kinds of products; and define the function responsible for managing and controlling storage areas. There should also be a policy stating that all storage areas must be designated, segregated, and identified by posted signs, and that storage of any products outside of designated storage areas is strictly prohibited.

Records

Records and evidence of compliance consist of the layout plans, procedures, and posted signs that document and identify the designation of specific areas for storage of particular kinds of products.

Audit

Assessing compliance, auditors will observe and note if all storage areas are clearly identified and segregated;

if they contain only the kinds of products for which they are designated; and if the storage areas are properly organized and maintained. Auditors will be also looking for products that are stored or held outside of the designated areas.

Requirement

Control receipt and dispatch of products to and from storage areas.

This requirement aims to prevent storage and issue of materials and products that could be different from those specified, or could be otherwise nonconforming. It is not, as many people think, a requirement for administrative measures to prevent theft or uncontrolled usage of materials. To comply, authorization to receive and dispatch products to and from storage areas should only be given when the products are clearly and completely identified, and have passed the prescribed inspections and tests. The authorization does not need to be explicitly given by a physical person every time products are placed in or removed from storage. Inspection sign-offs and/or passed inspection identification marking can provide implicit authorization. The authorization system can tie in with the general stock inventory management system.

Procedures

The operational procedure dealing with storage should stipulate what kind of authorization is required to admit and issue products to and from different storage areas, and, if explicit authorization is required for each receipt and dispatch, how and by whom it is given.

Records

If paperwork or an inventory management system is used for receipt and dispatch of products, the record will consist of authorizing sign-offs or appropriate database entries. Otherwise, the inspection status identification marking and inspection records provide the evidence of compliance.

Audit

Assessing compliance, auditors will review relevant operational procedures to verify that the receipt and dispatch authorization methods are clearly stipulated, and will audit their implementation.

Requirement

Regularly assess the condition of products in storage.

Stock should be reviewed at scheduled intervals to detect deteriorated or damaged products. The time interval should be set in relation to the shelf life of the products. The main issue is the removal of products with passed expiration dates and products damaged by corrosion, heat, moisture, etc.

Procedures

The operational procedure dealing with storage should stipulate the periodicity of stock assessments; assign the responsibility for this activity; and explain how to document the results of the assessments and communicate them to other functions concerned (for example, those that would decide if a corrective action should be requested).

Records

The stock assessment records provide evidence that the stock assessment has indeed been carried out, and report results of the assessment. Product nonconformance reports and corrective action reports provide additional evidence that results of the assessment are used to improve storage conditions and reduce the risk of product deterioration.

Audit

Assessing compliance, auditors will review the stock assessment records, and will verify that the assessments are conducted regularly as scheduled. They will also look for any damaged or deteriorated products in the storage areas. Auditors will expect that causes of product damage and deterioration are investigated and corrective actions are implemented when appropriate.

4.15.3.1   Inventory

Requirement

Establish and maintain an inventory management system.

This section explicitly requires that stocks be controlled using an inventory management system. In addition to tracking inventory, i.e. quantity and location of available stock, the system should also be used to minimize inventory levels and assure stock rotation. For this purpose, the system must be capable to report turnover times of stock, and provide information about the age and expiration dates of stock with limited shelf life.

Procedures

An appropriate operational procedure should assign the responsibility for maintaining the inventory management system, and define reporting requirements, including scope, frequency, and distribution of reports. On the wok instructions level, there must be a manual for operating the system (usually a computer database).

Records

Records and evidence of compliance are reports generated by the inventory management system.

Audit

Auditors will test the inventory system by selecting a sample of products in stock and checking that the quantity, location, and age of the sample items are correctly reported by the system. They may also do it the other way around; i.e., select a sample from the system and verify the information against the actual stock. Auditors will also review reports generated by the inventory system, and will ask how the system is used to minimize inventory levels and assure stock rotation.

4.15.4 Packaging

4.15.4.1 Customer Packaging Standards

4.15.4.2 Labeling

Requirement

Follow customer standards or specify requirements for packaging and labeling, and control these operations.

The packaging and materials used, and labeling should be formally defined in drawings, specifications, or standards. OEM customers normally have their own packaging and labeling standards. QS-9000 Section II, Customer-specific Requirements, lists the packaging and labeling standards for Chrysler, Ford, and General

Motors. When customers do not define their packaging requirements, suppliers must develop their own standards. Packaging specifications should be issued and be controlled in the same manner as product documentation. When packaging must meet certain performance criteria — such as strength, water- or airtightness, or electrostatic insulation — the packaging should be subjected to the same design, design verification, and process control procedures as apply to products.

Marking on packaging, to include product identification and shipping-related marking, should also be specified and controlled. The system for control of shipping packaging and marking should provide for communication and implementation of special customer or shipper requirements.

Procedures

The operational procedure that regulates the packaging operations should designate the function responsible for specification of packaging and marking; provide a system for communicating special packaging and marking requirements; and, where special packaging techniques or processes are used, reference the relevant work instructions.

Records

Records and evidence of compliance consist of the packaging drawings and specifications.

Audit

Assessing compliance, auditors will check if packaging is formally defined, and will verify that the actual packaging is the same as specified. When packaging requires special processes or techniques, auditors will assess the packaging operations against the same requirements that apply to production.

4.15.5 Preservation

Requirement

Apply appropriate methods for preservation and segregation of products.

Product preservation requirements are very similar to those that apply to product handling. In most companies no special preservation techniques are used. Products are simply protected against adverse atmospheric conditions and dirt. If this is the case, keeping products in dry and clean storage areas is sufficient to comply.

When special preservation methods and techniques are used — such as specially coated containers or tanks, engineered protective packaging, application of protective coating on exposed parts, or maintenance of specified temperature or humidity — the methods should be documented in procedures, specifications, and work instructions.

Procedures

When product preservation methods are routine and do not merit special operational procedure, they can be documented together with product handling (see the first requirement). The procedure should assign the responsibility for developing and implementing suitable product preservation methods; explain the basic requirements (dry and clean storage, use of protective packaging, etc.); and, when applicable, reference the specifications and work instructions for particular preservation methods.

Records

Product preservation activities usually do not require establishment of any records. However, when temperature, humidity, or other environmental conditions must be controlled, records are required to evidence that the environment is maintained within specified tolerances.

Audit

Assessing compliance, auditors will observe and note if products are adequately protected; if personnel follow work instructions when applying special preservation methods and techniques; and if there are any signs of products deteriorating, or being at risk, due to inadequate preservation.

4.15.6   Delivery

Requirement

Protect the quality of finished products to include delivery, when specified in contract.

If delivery is never specified in contracts, this requirement does not apply. If delivery is specified, but is always subcontracted, this requirement should be complied with by exercising the same kind of subcontractor qualification and monitoring controls that apply for purchasing of materials and components.

Companies that deliver themselves must have procedures explaining how products should be protected during delivery. The usual issues are loading techniques, stacking heights, fastening of loads, protection against rain, and so forth. When special protection techniques are used (for example, control of temperature, or engineered fastening of heavy loads), these should be documented in specifications or procedures.

Procedures

When delivery is not relevant or is always subcontracted, there is no need for operational procedure. It is sufficient to state in the quality manual that shippers are controlled in accordance with the same procedures that apply to subcontractors. When delivery is part of the operation, it should be regulated by a procedure. The procedure should assign the responsibility for developing and implementing suitable methods for protecting products during delivery; explain the basic methods (stacking, fastening, protection against rain, etc.); and, when applicable, reference the specifications and work instructions for special methods.

Records

There are normally no records of product protection during delivery, unless temperature or humidity control records are kept when applicable.

Audit

Assessing compliance, auditors will check if the subcontracted shippers are approved and if their quality performance is monitored. They may also want to observe the loading operations, whether delivery is subcontracted or not. In cases where special loading, protection, or transportation techniques are involved, auditors will use the same criteria that apply to process control.

4.15.6.1　　Supplier Delivery Performance Monitoring

Requirement

Establish a system to ensure consistent on-time delivery performance.

On-time delivery performance is a major concern in the automotive industries. QS-9000 added subsections to reinforce the original ISO 9000 requirements pertaining to on-time delivery. The required elements of the system for ensuring on-time delivery are:

- Order-driven production scheduling;
- Development of lead time requirements;
- Maintenance of premium freight records;
- On-time delivery performance monitoring;
- Investigation of late deliveries and implementation of corrective actions where appropriate; and
- Maintenance and use of a computerized system for receipt of customer planning information and ship schedules, and an Advance Shipment Notification (ASN) system.

In addition, there is a requirement in Section 4.6.2.2 for scheduling subcontractors to ensure on-time shipments of purchased materials and components, and for maintenance of premium freight records including both supplier and subcontractor paid charges.

Procedures

Appropriate operational procedure should outline the on-time delivery assurance system including all elements listed above. Specific elements may be developed in other procedures; for example, production scheduling and development of lead time requirements may be documented in a procedure dealing with production control, and implementation of corrective actions to improve delivery performance can be documented in the general corrective and preventive actions procedure.

Records

The relevant records and evidence of compliance are: on-time delivery statistics; evidence that all cases of late deliveries are investigated and that corrective actions are implemented when appropriate; lead time plans and requirements; production schedules; premium freight records; and evidence that the Advanced Shipment Notification system is properly operating and is used.

Audit

Assessing compliance, auditors will review the on-time delivery statistics and will verify them against shipping records, including premium freight records. For individual cases of late deliveries auditors will enquire about the causes and actions that may have been implemented to improve delivery performance. Auditors will also review production plans and verify that lead time requirements for design, purchasing, and production are determined and are documented.

4.15.6.2   Production Scheduling

Requirement

Use actual customer orders, rather than forecasts, in production scheduling.

This section reminds suppliers that forecasts are provided for general planning only, while the actual production schedules should be based on orders. When certain levels of inventory are normally maintained, production scheduling may also be based on replenishment of inventory, the so called "pull" system.

Procedures

Although this requirement is included in the section dealing with delivery, it may be best documented in procedures dealing with contract review and/or production planning. At the minimum, somewhere in the documentation there should be a statement that production scheduling shall be order-driven or based on replenishment of inventory, and that production should not be scheduled from customer forecasts.

Records

The evidence of conformance are current and historical production schedules.

Audit   Assessing compliance, auditors will ask directly how production schedules are established, and may want to compare current and past schedules to customer orders in the corresponding periods.

4.15.6.3   Electronic Communication

4.15.6.4   Shipment Notification System

Requirements in these sections are self explanatory. Suppliers must have computerized systems for receiving customer planning information and ship schedules, and an Advance Shipment Notification (ASN) system. There should also be a backup system if the ASN fails — a fax, for example. Both requirements can be waived by the customer.

* * * * *

Further reading

- Standard ISO 9004 Part 1, Sect. 10.4, 11.2, 16.1, 16.2
- J. Kanholm, *ISO 9000 Quality System*, Chap. 10 and Chap.. 12
- J. Kanholm, *QS-9000 Documentation*, QM Sect. 15, and Operational Procedures OOP-15-01, OOP-15-02, OOP-15-03, and OOP-15-04

16 CONTROL OF QUALITY RECORDS

4.16   Control of Quality Records

Application

This section applies to all records evidencing conformance and/or nonconformance of designs, materials, products, processes, personnel qualifications, and the quality system itself. A complete list of records required by QS-9000 is included in the appendix.

Some people confuse records and documents. *Records* are written statements of data and facts characterizing specific events that pertain to specific products, processes, persons, and so forth. *Documents* contain information and instructions. While most documents should be revised from time to time to account for changing requirements and conditions, records should never be changed. The requirements for document control are contained in Section 4.5.

Documentation

The quality manual should have a section dedicated to control of quality records. It should contain policies committing the company to manage and control quality records, and maintain them for a specified period of time. The manual should also contain a short outline procedure explaining how the policies are implemented, and reference the operational procedures that apply.

There must also be an operational procedure explaining the record management system, and stipulating retention periods for various types of records.

Requirement

Index and organize quality records to facilitate their retrieval.

Section 4.16 mentions identification, collection, indexing, access, filing, storage, maintenance, and disposition of quality records. All these words really mean one thing: retrievability. Any record management system will be accepted as long as it works. When a record has to be retrieved, it should be easily found and be legible and in good condition.

Records should be filed and stored in designated locations. Cabinets, drawers, shelves, and files containing records should be clearly labeled. Records should be arranged and indexed by product or other object that they concern, by event to which they pertain, or by date. When appropriate, the indexing should be cross-referenced. Specific function (person) should be assigned with the responsibility for maintaining record files.

Procedures

The operational procedure dealing with control of quality records should explain the policies and requirements for indexing, filing, and maintaining the records, and should assign the responsibility for these activities. Preservation and retrievability of records should be the ultimate objective of the record management system.

Records

There are no records required in this section. The evidence of compliance consists of the procedures and the implementation of the record management system.

Audit

The functioning of the quality record management system is continuously tested throughout the whole audit. Auditors will ask for retrieval of records when assessing almost any activity of the quality system. Records are often the only evidence that certain activities are taking place (for example: management reviews, design reviews, internal audits, corrective actions, training, and many others).

When auditors ask for a record, they will note how long it takes to retrieve it. If it happens that a record cannot be found immediately, it is best to tell the auditor right away that there will be some delay in retrieving the record, and encourage him or her to continue with the audit in the meantime. Nothing is more embarrassing and counterproductive than having the auditor wait and watch managers and staff frantically searching for a record.

When a record cannot be located at all, auditors will usually investigate the reason. If the problem is the lack of proper indexing and organization of records, there may be two noncompliances: one for the audited activity (lack of evidence of compliance) and the other for the breakdown of the record management system.

4.16.1   Record Retention

Requirement

Determine and document retention times for quality records.

QS-9000 Section 4.16.1 explicitly specifies minimum required retention times for records pertaining to part approvals, tooling, purchasing, process control, inspections and testing, internal quality audits, and management reviews.

For other types of records the retention times should be determined by the company. The determining factor is usually the life span of the object of the record. For example: Quality records pertaining to a product are usually stored and maintained for a period of time that relates to the product's estimated life or the warranty period, unless there are contractual, regulatory, or legal requirements that take precedence. Records pertaining to qualification and monitoring of subcontractors should be retained for as long as the subcontractor is used and/or the parts supplied by the subcontractor are active. Retention period for training records can be established on the basis of employment status, and so forth.

Records pertaining to periodical assessments, reviews, and certifications, such as internal quality audit reports, management review records, or calibration certificates, are usually kept for three cycles; i.e., records of annual events are kept for three years.

Procedures

The procedure dealing with the control of quality records should list all the categories of records and stipulate for each the retention time. For categories of records whose disposition depends on an event rather than just passage of time, the retention period can be defined in terms of the event instead of absolute time. For example, it can be stipulated that training records are retained for two years after termination of employment.

Records

No records are required. The evidence of compliance consists of the procedures documenting retention times for records, and the implementation of the procedures.

Audit

Assessing compliance, auditors will review the procedure stipulating retention times for records, and will ask for retrieval of some older records from various categories.

* * * * *

Further reading

- Standard ISO 9004 Part 1, Sect. 17
- J. Kanholm, *ISO 9000 Quality System*, Chap. 15
- J. Kanholm, *QS-9000 Documentation*, QM Sect. 16, and Operational Procedure QOP-16-01

17 INTERNAL QUALITY AUDITS

4.17
Application

Internal Quality Audits

Internal audit requirements apply to all activities comprising the quality system and all areas in the company where the system is implemented. An automotive requirement added to this section extends the scope of internal audits to also include assessment of the working environment. Working environment includes housekeeping, lighting, noise, temperature, ventilation, housekeeping-related safety hazards, etc. Product and process audits, understood as unscheduled complete layout inspections, are not included in the scope of this section.

Documentation

The quality manual should have a section dedicated to internal quality audits. It should contain policies committing the company to plan, conduct, and report internal audits, and to follow up with corrective actions to deal with deficiencies. The manual should also contain a short outline procedure explaining how the policies are implemented, and reference the operational procedures that apply.

There should also be an operational procedure explaining all aspects of the internal auditing system.

Requirement

Conduct internal audits using independent and qualified auditors.

Auditors must be independent from those responsible for the audited activity. In consequence, if the audits are usually conducted by the quality manager, someone else should be appointed to audit the quality assurance functions.

Qualifications of auditors should be evidenced by training records. These can be certificates from courses and seminars for auditors, or internal training provided by a consultant or someone in the company who is already qualified. Self-study training can also be accepted, but it must be formally recorded.

Auditors should prepare for each audit. The preparation may comprise review of the QS-9000 sections and quality system procedures relevant to the audited activity; and review of quality records, including audit reports from previous audits, corrective action requests, and product nonconformance reports.

It is recommended that auditors use checklists. The Quality System Assessment (QSA) automotive reference manual provides a standard checklist for auditing a QS-9000 quality system, and there are also audit checklist in Appendix A of the APQP manual. Preparing for the audit, auditors should review these standard checklists and supplement them to include questions pertaining to systems, activities, and current projects that are unique for the company. However, use of the QSA, or any other standard checklists, is not mandatory. There is no specified checklist that must be used. Internal auditors should focus on specific current and potential problems, rather than mechanically ticking off a standard checklist.

Procedures

The procedure for internal auditing should clearly state the policy that auditors must be independent; specify qualification and training requirements for auditors; and instruct how to prepare for, and conduct, the audit.

Records

Records and evidence of compliance are the auditor training and qualification records, and audit checklists, if these are retained. Also, the audit reports themselves will provide the evidence of auditor independence.

Audit

Assessing compliance, auditors may want to interview some internal auditors, questioning how they learned to conduct audits and how they prepare for an audit. Reviewing internal audit reports, auditors will also note if the assigned internal auditors are independent of the audited activity.

Requirement

Implement corrective actions to deal with identified deficiencies.

Every deficiency identified during an internal audit should automatically cause a request for corrective action. While in other circumstances the need for a corrective action can be evaluated and decided upon, there is no such freedom in the case of quality system audits. The quality system must comply with QS-9000 at all times, without exception.

For this reason, the internal audits, corrective action requests, and follow-up audits are usually integrated into one system. The forms used for reporting internal audits are adopted for processing all three phases.

But this integrated processing is the only difference. Otherwise, corrective actions resulting from internal audits must follow exactly the same rules that apply in general to corrective actions (see Section 14).

Procedures

The operational procedure dealing with internal audits should clearly state the policy that all identified deficiencies must be followed up by corrective actions. The procedure should explain the process and responsibilities for requesting, implementing, and verifying corrective actions, or refer to another procedure that already explains the corrective action initiation and implementation process (see Section 14).

Records

Records and evidence of compliance are the internal audit reports, in particular the sections reporting on corrective actions and follow-up audits.

Audit

Assessing compliance, auditors will review the internal audit reports, noting if corrective actions are being implemented in a timely manner, and if all are followed up by an audit to verify their implementation and effectiveness.

Requirement

Record and report the results of internal audits.

A popular system for reporting internal audits is based on a one-page form for recording and processing each individual noncompliance. The form is very similar to that used for processing and recording corrective actions. It has the following four blocks. *Heading*: for recording the particulars of the audit, such as identification of the audited location and activity, names of the auditor and the manager responsible for the audited area, etc. *Noncompliance*: for describing the noncomplying condition and classification of the noncompliance. *Corrective Action*: for describing the proposed action and the agreed implementation due date. *Follow up*: for recording the result of the follow-up audit and closing the noncompliance.

When a noncompliance is noted, the auditor fills out the *Heading* and the *Noncompliance* blocks, and passes the form to the manager responsible for the audited area, who uses the third block, *Corrective Action*, to propose a corrective action. On or shortly after the implementation due date, the auditor comes back to the area to verify that the corrective action has been implemented and that it is effective. The result of the follow-up audit is recorded in the last block of the form, *Follow up*. The final report for the audit can be put together by adding a cover page to the individual noncompliance reports. The cover page should provide audit particulars (date of the audit, audited areas, names of auditors, etc.) and a brief summary of audit results.

At the end of the auditing cycle, when all activities and areas have been audited, the partial audit reports should be bound together and submitted for review to the executive management. This is normally done in conjunction with the scheduled management reviews of the quality system (see Section 4.1). To facilitate the review, the final report should also contain statistics, conclusions, and recommendations.

Procedures

The operational procedure dealing with internal audits should explain how to use the audit noncompliance report forms; instruct how to prepare the final report for the whole audit cycle; assign the responsibility for preparing the report; and explain how the report should be submitted and/or presented for the management review.

Records

The records are, of course, the internal audit reports themselves.

Audit

Assessing compliance, auditors will review the internal audit reports, noting if they are established, processed, and evaluated by management in accordance with the governing procedures. A common problem with non-compliance reports is that corrective actions are not followed up in a timely manner.

4.17.1   Internal Audit Schedules

Requirement

Plan and schedule internal audits of the quality management system.

All activities comprising the quality system should be audited at least once a year. Quality systems under implementation, and for the first year or two of operation, should be audited more frequently: every three or six months, for example. Even for mature systems, those activities that are especially important should be audited more frequently. QS-9000 requires also that audit frequency should be increased for activities where there are internal or external nonconformances or customer complains. The internal audit can be carried out all at once, as certification audits are, or be distributed throughout the whole auditing cycle. The distributed way is preferable in most cases.

A popular format for an audit plan is a matrix with vertical listings of all quality system elements (activities) and horizontal listings of all departments and areas in the company. In the blocks where the elements and areas intersect, the planned audit dates can be written in or, if a given activity is not relevant in an area, the block can be crossed out. This format ensures that all quality system elements will be audited in all relevant areas; i.e., that nothing will be missed. Certification auditors use such matrices when planning their audits.

Procedures

The procedure dealing with internal audits should explain what criteria need to be applied when planning internal audits; how to establish and document the audit plan; and who is responsible for establishing the plan and monitoring its execution.

Records

There are no records of this activity, other than the internal audit plan itself.

Audit

Auditing compliance, auditors will review the internal audit plan, noting if all relevant activities and areas are included, and if the frequency of auditing reflects the maturity of the quality system, the importance of individual elements, and the history of internal or external nonconformances and customer complaints.

* * * * *

Further reading

- Standard ISO 9004 Part 1, Sect. 5.4
- J. Kanholm, *ISO 9000 Quality System*, Chap. 16
- J. Kanholm, *QS-9000 Documentation*, QM Sect. 17, and Operational Procedures QOP-17-01 and AOP-01-03

18 TRAINING

4.18   Training

Application

In the original ISO 9000 standard training requirements apply to all personnel performing activities affecting quality. QS-9000 extends the application of training requirements to all personnel, without exception.

Documentation

The quality manual should have a section dedicated to training. It should contain policies committing the company to identify training needs, provide for the required training, maintain training records, and verify effectiveness of training. The manual should also contain a short outline procedure explaining how the policies are implemented, and reference the operational procedures that apply.

There should also be an operational procedure explaining all aspects of the training system.

Requirement

Identify training needs for all personnel.

The examples of situations that can create a need for personnel training are: new-hired personnel who do not have sufficient education, skills, or experience; personnel who do not perform their work satisfactorily; introduction of new methods, technologies, and management systems; and the desire to improve communication, motivation, productivity, or quality awareness. Human resources and departmental managers should be instructed to identify these and other such situations, and respond with appropriate training programs.

The system for identifying training needs can operate on two levels. One is local, where the competence and/or skill level of personnel is regularly evaluated against defined criteria and requirements. The other is central, where training is used as a tool for implementing company-wide policies. For example, each departmental manager can be responsible for training his or her own personnel in the skills and techniques used in the department, while human resources can be responsible for training all personnel in areas such as communication, motivation, and quality awareness.

The system should also allow personnel to make requests for training, or allow support of external training to satisfy individual training needs.

While the standard does not specify any training as mandatory, auditors expect that personnel carrying out inspections and tests be trained in the use of measuring equipment, inspection techniques, and application of statistical methods; process operators be trained in carrying out their processes and monitoring process performance (SPC); and all personnel be trained in the use and maintenance of the quality system.

Procedures

The operational procedure dealing with training should have a section dedicated to identification of training needs. The procedure should divide training into relevant categories, and assign the responsibility for identifying training needs in each category. The procedure should also provide a system for requesting internal or external training, and assign the responsibility for reviewing the requests. Where relevant, specific methods for periodical evaluation of personnel qualifications can also be included in the procedure.

Records

Identification of training needs usually does not require establishment of any records. However, in cases where requests for training are being formally submitted and processed, and where personnel qualifications are regularly evaluated, there will be some paper trail evidencing that training needs are being identified.

Audit

When there are no records of the training needs identification activities, auditors will rely on interviewing managers and personnel to check if training needs are being actively identified. They will ask for examples of specific cases when individuals were trained or retrained to meet the qualification requirements applicable to their positions, and will verify that company-wide training programs are being established and implemented, especially quality system training.

Requirement

Provide for the required training and maintain training records.

Training can be provided in many ways. It can be a simple demonstration of how to operate a machine; on-the-job assistance and monitoring; practicing skills on samples and simulators; theoretical classroom lecturing; external courses and seminars; and self-study from books, articles, or video courses. Regardless of the form and duration, training should always be formally documented and recorded.

Training documentation should provide information about the content, scope, duration, and form of training. Based on the documentation alone, it should be possible to make an accurate assumption of what knowledge and skills can be expected from the trained person. Just mentioning the title of a course is not sufficient. Whenever possible, a copy of the materials used in training should be retained for documentation purposes.

Companies preparing for QS-9000 certification that previously did not have a formalized training system, and did not kept training records, can grandfather their existing personnel. Training records can be substituted by certificates confirming their qualifications.

Procedures

The operational procedure dealing with training should assign the responsibility for providing training in different areas and categories. It should also outline the applicable forms of training, and explain for each the requirements regarding instructor qualifications, documentation of content, and establishment of records. If the company has permanent training programs, such as general orientation or quality system training, it should also be documented in the procedure.

Records

Training records can be diploma, certificates, licenses, experience resumes, lists of training attendance, or any other documents evidencing qualifications and skills. All forms of training should be recorded, including demonstrations, on-the-job training, and self-study. The records can be kept centrally by the human resources department, for example, or be filed locally with the department that provided training.

Audit

Assessing compliance, auditors will review the training program, the documentation of training provided, and the training records; and will interview personnel, asking how they learned the skills required in their positions. Auditors will verify that the training program is sufficient; i.e., at a minimum comprises inspection-related functions, process operators, and quality system orientation for everybody; that the content, form, and duration of training are documented; that instructors are themselves sufficiently qualified; and that proper training records are being established.

4.18.1   Training Effectiveness

Requirement

Periodically evaluate training effectiveness.

This section requires that the effectiveness of training be periodically reviewed. In this case, *reviewed* means evaluated, assessed or verified. In practice, for every training provided there must be a recorded assessment whether the training was effective; i.e., whether the training resulted in better performance.

One practical method that could be used is an annual review of the training program conducted by departmental managers or supervisors. Every training course provided through the year is reviewed. Results of the review are recorded and are used as feedback for revising and updating the training program. Another method is a periodical appraisal of individual employees combined with effectiveness evaluation of the training they received. Results of internal audits and company-level

statistical data that can be linked to employee performance may also be used for evaluating training effectiveness.

Procedures

Appropriate operational procedure should outline the
methods used for training evaluation in various departments and training categories. If every department
wants to use its own system, details can be documented locally on work instruction level. The procedure should
assign the responsibility for training evaluation, explain
the process, and instruct how to establish the evaluation
records. There should also be a requirement for communicating the training evaluation results to those concerned with specifying and providing training.

Records

Although QS-9000 does not explicitly require that training evaluation results must be recorded, it will be difficult to prove compliance if there are no records at all.
Without records there is also a problem with communicating the evaluation results to others, especially in larger companies. The format of the record will depend on the
evaluation method. Records can be in a form of memoranda, minutes of meetings, logs, sign-off sheets, etc.

Audit

Assessing compliance, auditors will enquire about the
methods used for evaluating training effectiveness, and
will choose a sample of specific training programs and ask
for the evidence that effectiveness of these programs was
evaluated. Auditors will also verify that effectiveness
evaluation is conducted for all types of company-wide
and departmental training programs, without exception.

* * * * *

Further reading

- Standard ISO 9004 Part 1, Sect. 18
- J. Kanholm, *ISO 9000 Quality System*, Chap. 14
- J. Kanholm, *QS-9000 Documentation*, QM Sect. 18,
  and Operational Procedure AOP-18-01

19 SERVICING

4.19 Servicing

Application

Servicing is named in the title of the standard, and there should not be any need for this section at all — especially because it does not contain any specific requirements. Installation is also named in the title, but it does not have its own section. Whatever the purpose of this section, it is clear that all relevant requirements of the standard must be applied to servicing operations and activities, just as they apply to design, development, production, and installation.

Documentation

If there are no servicing operations and activities, this should be stated in the quality manual. Nothing else needs to be done to comply with this section. When servicing is carried out, but it is only a peripheral activity, the quality manual should have a section dedicated to servicing. It should contain policies committing the company to apply all relevant QS-9000 requirements to the servicing operations; a short outline procedure explaining how the policies are implemented; and references to the operational procedures that apply. When servicing is an important or principal activity, every relevant section of the quality manual should refer to servicing.

The number of procedures regulating the servicing operations can vary from just one, generally explaining how the quality system is applied to servicing, to 20 or more, documenting the whole quality system when servicing is the major, or the only, activity in the company.

Requirement

Apply all requirements of the standard to servicing operations and activities.

While in theory all requirements of the standard apply, the most relevant are those that pertain to control of spare parts, the control of servicing processes, and verification of servicing. Spare parts used in servicing should be new or, when reconditioned parts are used, they should be inspected to ensure that they fully comply with the original specifications. Unidentified and unauthorized parts should not be stored in servicing areas. The control of servicing processes should comply with the same requirements that apply to production processes. Serviced products should not be released before the servicing is inspected and/or the products tested.

Procedures

In a company where servicing is only a peripheral activity, it is sufficient to have only one operational procedure dealing with servicing. The procedure should reference other relevant procedures that apply (for example, contract review, purchasing, process control, inspections, etc.) and provide new instructions only in areas where the quality systems in production and servicing differ substantially.

Records

All requirements for establishment and maintenance of records are the same as those that apply to production activities. But the most important records are probably the final inspection records.

Audit

Assessing compliance, auditors will proceed very differently when servicing is only a peripheral activity compared to when it is the principal business. In the first case, they will focus mainly on the management and control of spare parts, general process control, and inspection activities. In the other case, servicing will be the object of the whole audit.

4.19.1   Feedback of Information from Service

Requirement

Feedback service concerns to engineering and production.

This section requires that information on product performance, reliability, serviceability, and other such service concerns should be communicated to engineering and production. This can be done in a form of reports, memoranda, statistics of common problems, and so forth. The standard does not prescribe any specific scope of, or method for, communicating the information.

Procedures

Procedure for communicating service concerns is explicitly required. The procedure should instruct what kinds of information and data are collected, how information is processed and reported, and how it is communicated to other functions concerned. There should also be instructions pertaining to the review and use of the information.

Records

Records and evidence of compliance are the reports, memoranda, and statistics established by service; and the evidence that the information is transmitted to engineering and production.

Audit

Auditors will verify that the information on service concerns is collected, reported, and transmitted regularly, and that the information is reviewed and used by engineering and production. They will also verify that the information is transmitted in the manner prescribed by the procedure (a procedure is explicitly required).

* * * * *

Further reading

- Standard ISO 9004 Part 1, Sect. 16.4
- J. Kanholm, *ISO 9000 Quality System*, Chap. 13
- J. Kanholm, *QS-9000 Procedures*, QM Sect. 19, and Operational Procedure OOP-19-01

20 STATISTICAL TECHNIQUES

4.20

Application

Statistical Techniques

Statistical techniques should be applied to evaluating, controlling, and verifying production processes; evaluating measurement systems; setting up process equipment; sampling for inspection and testing; validating designs; analyzing quality performance and other company-level data; and other activities where statistical methods can be successfully applied.

Documentation

The quality manual should have a section dedicated to statistical techniques. It should contain policies committing the company to identify the need for statistical techniques and to apply them in relevant activities, and provide a short outline procedure explaining how the policies are implemented. The manual should also reference the procedures and work instructions that apply.

There is usually no need for an operational procedure. Particular procedures pertaining to activities where statistical techniques are used should explain the applicable techniques, or refer to appropriate work instructions or standards.

4.20.1

4.20.2

Identification of Need

Procedures

Requirement

Identify the need for statistical techniques, establish procedures for their selection and application, and train personnel in basic statistical concepts.

QS-9000 explicitly require the use of statistical techniques in evaluating process capability, monitoring process performance, verifying process equipment setups, and evaluating measurement systems. In addition, the company should identify the need for statistical techniques in such applications as analysis of prototype testing data; processing of quality performance, productivity, and customer satisfaction data; establishment of sampling plans for receiving and in-process inspections, and so forth. The authority and methods for selecting appropriate statistical techniques for different activities are usually documented in procedures dealing with those activities. Process operators must be familiar with basic statistical concepts.

Procedures

Usually there is no need for a dedicated operational procedure dealing with application of statistical techniques. The applicable techniques can be documented directly in relevant process control and inspection procedures, usually issued on the work instruction level. They can also be defined by references to applicable standards, automotive reference manuals, and text books.

Records

Records and evidence of compliance consist of those process control records, inspection records, measurement system evaluation reports, etc., where statistical techniques are used. There should also be training records evidencing that process operators are familiar with basic statistical concepts.

Audit

Assessing compliance, auditors will review the procedures instructing in the use of statistical techniques, and will verify that the techniques are indeed implemented. Auditors will also interview process operators to verify that they are familiar with statistical concepts.

* * * * *

Further reading

- Standard ISO 9004 Part 1, Sect. 20
- J. Kanholm, *ISO 9000 Quality System*, Chap. 10 and Chap. 11
- J. Kanholm, *QS-9000 Documentation*, QM Sect. 20, and Oper. Proc. OOP-09-04 and QOP-11-02

APPENDIX

The following documents, records, and evidence of compliance will be reviewed by auditors during the QS-9000 certification audit. Not all of the documents and records are directly named in the standards but, when applicable, all will be expected. Because a procedure is called out does not mean that it always needs to be an independent operational procedure; it can be a section in the quality manual or another procedure, or a work instruction.

Sect.	Documents	Evidence of Compliance
4.1	■ Quality policy (QM) ■ Organizational charts (QM-1) ■ Appointment of management representative (QM-1) ■ Procedure explaining how management reviews of quality system are conducted and recorded (AOP-01-03) ■ Procedure explaining how business plan is established, tracked, and updated (AOP-01-01, AOP-01-03) ■ Procedure explaining how to collect, analyze, and use company-level quality performance data (QOP-02-07, AOP-01-03) ■ Procedure explaining how to determine customer satisfaction and appropriate benchmarks (AOP-01-02, AOP-01-03) ■ Assignment of responsibility and authority for notifying certification authority (registrar) when customer downgrades site status (QM-1)	■ Records evidencing that the effectiveness and suitability of the quality system is regularly assessed ■ Business plan and evidence that the plan is regularly reviewed, tracked, and updated ■ Charts, reports, etc. showing trends in company-level quality performance data, and evidence that the data is regularly reviewed by management ■ Charts, reports, etc. showing customer satisfaction levels, and evidence that the data is regularly reviewed by management ■ If relevant, records demonstrating that certification authority (registrar) has been notified of customer downgrading site status
4.2	■ Quality system manual ■ Operational procedures	
4.2.3	■ Procedure explaining how product quality is planned in design and prototype, pre-launch, and production phases; and how the plan is carried	■ Evidence that multi-disciplinary quality planning team actively participates in quality planning (minutes of meetings, sign-offs on documents, etc.)

Sect.	Documents	Evidence of Compliance
4.2.3 cont.	out (QOP-02-01, QOP-02-02, QOP-02-03, QOP-02-04) ■ Procedure documenting composition of a cross-functional quality planning team, and explaining how the team operates (QOP-02-01, QOP-02-02, QOP-02-03, QOP-02-04) ■ Procedure explaining how special characteristics are determined and documented (QOP-02-02, QOP-02-03) ■ Procedure explaining how to conduct and document product and process FMEAs (QOP-02-02, QOP-02-03, EOP-04-01) ■ Procedure explaining how to prepare Control Plans for prototype, pre-launch and production phases (QOP-02-02, QOP-02-03, QOP-02-04) ■ Policies and procedures for promoting awareness of product safety aspects (QM-2.2, AOP-18-01)	■ Team feasibility commitment ■ List of special characteristics ■ Control Plans for prototype, pre-launch, and production phases ■ Product and process FMEAs ■ Process flowcharts ■ Preliminary process capability studies ■ Measurement system evaluation reports ■ Complete layout inspection reports ■ Material and performance testing reports ■ Process operator instructions ■ Product quality planning sign-off ■ Evidence that mistake proofing methods are used ■ All relevant records from the product quality planning process
4.2.4	■ Procedures for coordinating the PPAP process, and explaining how to prepare individual PPAP items (QM Section 2.3, QOP-02-05, QOP-02-02, QOP-02-03, QOP-02-04, EOP-04-01, and others) ■ Procedure for subcontractor part approval process (QOP-02-06)	■ All submission items required by the PPAP Reference Manual ■ Subcontractor part approval submission items and evidence that they are being reviewed
4.2.5	■ Procedure for identifying improvement opportunities (QOP-02-07) ■ Procedure for initiating, carrying out, and reporting improvement projects (QOP-02-07)	■ Evidence that performance is tracked and evaluated to identify opportunities for improvement ■ Specific action plans for continuous improvement of processes ■ Evidence that there is knowledge of specific improvement methodologies ■ Improvement project files
4.2.6	■ Procedure for developing appropriate manufacturing facilities, processes and equipment (QOP-02-02, QOP-02-03, QOP-02-04)	■ Evidence that existing operations are evaluated

Sect.	Documents	Evidence of Compliance
	■ Procedure for tooling management (OOP-02-08)	■ Tooling drawings and design records ■ Tooling lists, status logs and records
4.3	■ Procedure and/or checklist for contract (order) review (MOP-03-02) ■ Procedure explaining how to process change orders (MOP-03-02)	■ Offers, contracts, etc. displaying evidence (stamp, sign-off) that they have been reviewed and approved; or other records of contract review ■ Team feasibility commitment ■ Paper trails (memos, transmittal letters, etc.) evidencing that change order requirements are effectively communicated to functions concerned
4.4	All below-listed procedures are included in EOP-04-01: ■ Procedure explaining how design projects are planned; including scheduling, activity assignment, and control of technical interfaces ■ Procedure instructing how to document, review, and approve design input ■ Procedure for validating and controlling computer software ■ Procedure explaining how to conduct design reviews ■ Procedure explaining how to document design output and how to issue and control engineering documents, including control of computer files (disk labeling, storage, backups, security, etc.) ■ Procedure explaining how to verify design output (may include review and verification checklists) ■ Procedure for prototype build and testing (when required) ■ Procedure for design change processing and approval	■ Documented design input and evidence that the design input has been reviewed and approved ■ Evidence that CAD/CAE systems are used in design, and that the computer systems can interface with customer's systems ■ Design project schedule and activity assignment ■ Evidence that personnel assigned with design activities are qualified in applicable skills and design techniques (see QS-9000 Sect. 4.4.2) ■ Software validation reports ■ Design FMEAs ■ Design output engineering documents, and evidence that the documents are reviewed, checked, and approved prior to release ■ Backup disks and other evidence that computer files are properly managed and controlled ■ Reports, calculations, sign-offs, etc. evidencing that design is verified before release ■ Records of design reviews ■ Prototype program and prototype testing reports (when required) ■ ECRs and evidence that design changes are approved by customer

Sect.	Documents	Evidence of Compliance
4.5	• Scope of the document control system, i.e., definition of which types of documents are controlled (QOP-05-01) • Procedure explaining how various types of documents are issued, distributed, and revised (QOP-05-02) • Procedure explaining control of documents in electronic media, i.e., computer files (QOP-05-02) • Document distribution lists or placement locations for QM, procedures, and all other types of controlled documents	• Evidence that documents are reviewed and approved prior to release (release sign-offs) • Master list or other means for verifying current revision level of a document • Backup logs and disks, and other evidence that documents in electronic media are properly controlled • Sign-off evidencing approval of handwritten changes in controlled documents • Document distribution logs (records) • Marking and segregation of historical (obsolete) documents • Identification of changes in revised documents
4.6	• Procedure explaining how subcontractors are selected and prequalified, and how their quality performance is monitored, including on-time delivery (OOP-06-01) • Policy or procedure expressing commitment to develop subcontractors using QS-9000 (OOP-06-01) • Procedure instructing how to establish, review, and approve purchasing documents (OOP-06-02) • Procedure documenting the process to assure that governmental regulations for restricted and hazardous substances are complied with • Approved subcontractor list	• Subcontractor quality record files containing documents supporting their prequalification, and records of their quality performance • Evidence that subcontractors are developed using QS-9000 • Records of subcontractor on-time delivery performance • Evidence that safety and handling instructions, etc. are required with purchase of hazardous substances • Purchase orders and contracts • Records demonstrating that purchasing documents are reviewed and approved prior to release
4.7	• Procedure explaining how to receive, identify, store, and maintain customer-supplied product, including tooling and returnable packaging (MOP-07-01)	• There are usually no special records (other than inventory) of customer-owned products • When product is lost, damaged, or is otherwise unsuitable, there must be evidence that customer has been informed

Sect.	Documents	Evidence of Compliance
4.8	▪ Procedure explaining how products are identified (OOP-08-01) ▪ Procedure documenting traceability systems (OOP-08-01) ▪ Bills of materials ▪ Parts lists	▪ Logs, database, lists, etc. with assignment of part numbers ▪ Material and process traceability records (may be production work order)
4.9	▪ Procedure for establishing, distributing, and using process operator instructions (OOP-09-02) ▪ Procedure explaining how to carry out preliminary process capability studies (OOP-09-03) ▪ Procedure instructing in ongoing process performance monitoring, i.e., statistical process control and charting (OOP-09-03) ▪ Procedure documenting preventive maintenance system, including preventive maintenance plans and schedules (OOP-09-04) ▪ Procedure for verification of job set-ups (QOP-10-02) ▪ Procedure explaining requirements for manufacturing and inspecting "Appearance Items" (QOP-10-02)	▪ Process operator instructions ▪ Preliminary process capability studies ▪ Process control charts ▪ Equipment maintenance logs and reports ▪ Job set-up instructions and set-up verification charts ▪ Production schedules ▪ Production work orders, travelers, or other production records
4.10	▪ Procedure explaining when and how incoming product is inspected (QOP-10-01) ▪ Procedures for in-process controls, monitoring, and inspections (QOP-10-02) ▪ Procedure for final inspection and product release (QOP-10-03) ▪ Procedure for layout inspection and functional testing (QOP-10-03) ▪ Procedure for a quality system in testing and calibration laboratories (QOP-10-04) ▪ Specific inspection, testing and calibration instructions and checklists	▪ Control plans for receiving, in-process and final inspection ▪ Subcontractor quality system certification, inspection and testing reports, etc., when incoming product is not inspected ▪ Receiving inspection records ▪ In-process control, monitoring and inspection records ▪ Final inspection and product release records ▪ Layout inspection and functional testing records ▪ Laboratory records

Sect.	Documents	Evidence of Compliance
4.11	■ Procedure explaining how measuring and testing equipment is identified, controlled, and maintained (QOP-11-01) ■ Procedure documenting calibration and calibration control system (QOP-11-01) ■ Procedure explaining how to conduct measurement system analysis (QOP-11-02) ■ Specific calibration instructions	■ Measurement and test equipment inventory list or database ■ Equipment calibration certificates ■ Reports of measurement system analysis
4.12	■ Procedure explaining the system for identifying inspection status of materials and products (QOP-12-01)	■ Evidence of implementation, such as tags, labels, and other marking applied to products to identify their inspection status (may be also traveling work order or other documents accompanying products)
4.13	■ Procedure explaining how nonconforming product is identified and documented (QOP-13-01) ■ Procedure explaining who makes nonconforming product disposition decisions, and how (QOP-13-01) ■ Procedure for requesting EAPAs (QOP-13-01) ■ Procedure for control of reworked products (QOP-13-01)	■ Product nonconformance reports ■ Evidence that nonconformance reports are closed out in a timely manner, and that corrective actions are initiated when appropriate ■ Customer EAPAs and records showing authorized quantities and/or expiration dates ■ Product rework instructions, and reinspection records
4.14	■ Procedure explaining how corrective actions are initiated, processed, and closed out (QOP-14-01) ■ Procedure explaining how the need for preventive actions is identified, and how preventive actions are processed (QOP-14-01) ■ Procedure for testing and analyzing customer returned products (QOP-14-01) ■ Procedure for receiving, processing, and responding to customer complaints (QOP-14-02)	■ Corrective and preventive action records (CARs, follow-ups, etc.) ■ Evidence that company level quality performance data are regularly reviewed to identify the need for preventive action ■ Returned product testing and analysis reports ■ Customer complaints files ■ Evidence that corrective/preventive actions and customer complaints are processed in a timely manner

Sect.	Documents	Evidence of Compliance
4.15	▪ Procedure for product handling and preservation (OOP-15-01) ▪ Specific handling and preservation instructions ▪ Procedure regulating the operation of storage and holding areas, including inventory control system (OOP-15-02) ▪ Procedure for packaging and labeling (OOP-15-03) ▪ Packaging specifications and packaging instructions ▪ Procedure for shipping and delivery, including system for ensuring on-time delivery (OOP-15-04) ▪ Procedure explaining the shipment notification system (OOP-15-04)	▪ Inventory logs, lists, or databases ▪ Assessment of stock reports ▪ Product shelf life identification ▪ Shipping orders, bills, and records ▪ On-time delivery performance records
4.16	▪ Procedure specifying which records are maintained and what is their retention period (QOP-16-01)	▪ Evidence that records are properly established, are appropriately stored, are retrievable, and are retained for the specified retention period
4.17	▪ Procedure explaining how internal audits are planned, conducted, reported, and followed up, and how their results are reported to the executive management (QOP-17-01) and (AOP-01-03)	▪ Internal audit plan ▪ Audit reports and checklists ▪ Auditor qualification records ▪ Evidence that corrective actions are implemented and followed up
4.18	▪ Procedure explaining how training needs are identified (AOP-18-01) ▪ Internal and external training programs and policies (AOP-18-01) ▪ Procedure for evaluating training effectiveness (AOP-18-01)	▪ Training specifications and briefs ▪ Employee training records ▪ Training evaluation reports
4.19	▪ Procedure regulating servicing operations (OOP-19-01) ▪ Procedure explaining how field experience and reliability data are communicated to manufacturing, engineering, and design (OOP-19-01)	▪ All records established by servicing function, such as servicing orders, defect tests and analysis reports, verification of serviced products, etc. ▪ Reports with field experience and reliability data, and evidence that the information is communicated

Sect.	Documents	Evidence of Compliance
4.20	■ Procedure explaining where and when statistical techniques are used, and how to select appropriate techniques (QM Section 20) ■ Instructions on how to use specific statistical techniques (OOP-09-04)	■ Examples of charts, analysis, and reports where statistical techniques are used ■ Evidence that basic statistical concepts are understood throughout the organization, as appropriate

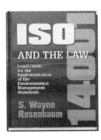

ISO 9000 by Jack Kanholm

ISO 9000 QUALITY MANUAL AND 32 PROCEDURES

Third Edition

Book and computer software with quality manual, procedures and forms - $ 290.

This computer software is a unique resource for documenting an ISO 9000 quality management system. It offers:

- A quality system that is simple, natural and free from excessive paperwork, and satisfies certification requirements.
- Fully developed two-level documentation, including the quality manual, operational procedures and forms.
- Computer templates for procedures and forms (in Microsoft Word or WordPerfect).

Thousands of companies have been successfully certified using this documentation (first published in 1992).

ISO 9000 REQUIREMENTS

72 Requirements Checklist and Compliance Guide

Third Edition

136 Pages
Hardcover Book - $ 49.

This book identifies 72 distinct, auditable requirements in ISO 9001 and ISO 9002 standards. Each requirement is explained with regard to interpretation, procedures, records, and relevant auditing practices. In essence, the book reinterprets the standards into a list of 72 specific actions that need to be taken to achieve conformance, and explains how to implement them in the organization. Now in its third edition, and with over 30,000 copies sold, this book is established as the reference of choice for understanding and interpreting the ISO 9000 standards.

Department by department this book explains precisely what a company must do to implement the ISO 9000 quality system and pass the certification audit. There are hundreds of tips and examples of implementation solutions. There are also examples of audit situations illustrating what auditors will be looking for, what auditing techniques they will use, and how they will react in specific situations. It's like having a first class consultant and an auditor assist you with your ISO 9000 implementation project.

ISO 9000 QUALITY SYSTEM

Department by Department Implementation for the Certification Audit

228 Pages
Hardcover Book - $ 69.

This is a general orientation course for ISO 9000. The workbook is intended for distribution to all personnel for self-study or group training. The course explains what the ISO 9000 standards are, how the quality system works, and how everyone should prepare themselves and their work areas for the certification audit. This course satisfies ISO 9000 requirements for training personnel in the quality system. It includes a short test and a certificate of completion.

ISO 9000 IN OUR COMPANY

Self-Study Course for Personnel

Third Edition

32 Pages Booklet - $ 9.

SATISFIED CUSTOMERS This ISO 9000 series was initially published in 1992 — the first in the USA. Over 27,000 companies have purchase these materials and some 80% have ordered additional copies or recommended the books to others. The lasting popularity of these materials is their best recommendation.

More info on the internet at www.AQAco.com

ISO 13485 & EN 46000

by Lynette Howard and Jack Kanholm

ISO 13485 (EN 46000) QUALITY SYSTEM MANUAL AND 36 PROCEDURES

Book and computer software with quality manual, procedures and forms - $ 390.

ISO 13485 (EN 46000) REQUIREMENTS

99 Requirements Checklist and Compliance Guide

170 Pages
Hardcover Book - $ 59.

ISO 13485 (EN 46000) IN OUR COMPANY

Self-Study Course for Personnel

32-Page Booklet, Test and Certificate - $ 9.

QUALITY SYSTEM FOR THE MEDICAL DEVICE INDUSTRY

The three publications in this series provide: ready-made template documentation with the quality manual and operational procedures, explanation of all ISO 13485 and EN 46000 requirements, and a general orientation course for personnel. All three publications are based on Jack Kanholm's ISO 9000 series (refer to the preceding page annotating the ISO 9000 publications).

Ms. Howard contributed her unique knowledge of both the U.S. and European regulatory requirements and certification systems.

QS-9000 by Jack Kanholm

QS-9000 QUALITY SYSTEM MANUAL AND 40 PROCEDURES

Book and computer software with quality manual, procedures and forms - $ 390.

QS-9000 REQUIREMENTS

107 Requirements Checklist and Compliance Guide

177 Pages
Hardcover Book - $ 59.

QS-9000 IN OUR COMPANY

Self-Study Course for Personnel

32-Page Booklet, Test and Certificate - $ 9.

QUALITY SYSTEM FOR THE AUTOMOTIVE INDUSTRY

The three publications in this series provide: ready-made template documentation with the quality manual and operational procedures, explanation of all QS-9000 requirements, and a QS-9000 general orientation course for personnel. All three publications are based on Jack Kanholm's ISO 9000 series (refer to the preceding page annotating the ISO 9000 publications).

Since 1995 thousands of companies have used these materials to successfully achieve QS-9000 certification.

O R D E R   F O R M

Qty	Title	Prc	Dsc	Total	Qty	Title	Prc	Dsc	Total
	ISO 9000					**ISO 14000**			
	ISO 9000 Requirements	$ 49.	%			ISO 14001 Requirements	$ 49.	%	
	ISO 9000 Quality System	$ 69.	%			ISO 14001 And The Law	$ 59.	%	
	ISO 9000 In Our Company	$ 9.	%			ISO 14001 In Our Company	$ 9.	%	.
	ISO 9000 Template Manual and Procedures Software	$ 290.	%			ISO 14001 Template Manual and Procedures Software	$ 290.	%	
	QS-9000					**ISO 13485 (EN 46000)**			
	QS-9000 Requirements	$ 59.	%			ISO 13485 Requirements	$ 59.	%	
	QS-9000 In Our Company	$ 9.	%			ISO 13485 In Our Company	$ 9.	%	
	QS-9000 Template Manual and Procedures Software	$ 390.	%			ISO 13485 Template Manual and Procedures Software	$ 390.	%	

Sales tax of 7.75% (CA only) and shipping cost (see chart below) will be added to invoice

Quantity Discounts (copies per title)	**Shipping (by UPS)**
5 to 9: 10% 20 to 39: 30% Over 100: 50% 10 to 19: 20% 40 to 99: 40%	❑ Ground $ 6. ❑ 2nd Day $ 13. ❑ 3rd Day $ 9. ❑ Next Day $ 25.

Shipping Address (No PO Boxes)

Mr. ❑   Ms. ❑

Title: _____

Company: _____

Street: _____

City: _____ State: ____ Zip: ____

Phone & Fax: _____

Billing Address

Company: _____

Street: _____

City: _____ State: ____ Zip: ____

Attention: _____

Method of Payment

Card No.: | | | | | | | | | | | | | | | | |

❑ Check ❑ Visa ❑ MC ❑ AmEx Exp.: _____

❑ Bill Company Purchase Order No.: _____

Signature & Date: _____

30 Day Preview

❑ Yes, I want to preview the publications and reserve the right to return them for a refund (excluding shipping cost), if not satisfied.
I understand that to receive a refund, I must return the publications within 30 days.

To order, fax this form to (626) 796 9070 or call (800) 600 3601